FABER'S
ANATOMICAL ATLAS

FABER'S ANATOMICAL ATLAS

Edited by

IAN M. BURDON
M.B., Ch.B., F.R.C.S. (Ed.)

and

S. MACDONALD
S.R.N.

Revised by

JOHN McKENZIE
M.D.

Senior Lecturer, Department of Anatomy,
University of Aberdeen

Plates by

A. K. MAXWELL

FABER AND FABER
3 QUEEN SQUARE
LONDON

Fourth edition published in 1962
by Faber and Faber Limited
3 Queen Square London W.C.1
First published in this edition 1964
Reprinted 1965, 1968, 1970, 1974 and 1977
Printed in Great Britain by
Robert MacLehose and Company Limited
Printers to the University of Glasgow

ISBN 0 571 06461 2 (Faber Paperbacks)
ISBN 0 571 05107 3 (hard bound edition)

CONTENTS

PLATES

TEXT

FOREWORD

THE aim of this Atlas is to provide the student with a clear picture of the human body, preparatory to the subsequent study of the abnormal.

It has been considered sufficient merely to mention in the text points that are clearly demonstrated by the diagrams, but necessary detail that cannot be exhibited in the drawings has been dealt with more fully.

A certain amount of physiology has been included from the point of view of interest and to convey a more thorough understanding of the causes and treatment of many diseases.

I. B.
S. M.

PREFACE

IN spite of extensive revision and the insertion of new illustrations, the aim of this book is unchanged.

Essentially an atlas with an explanatory text, it is comprehensive in scope and intended for students who have not the opportunity or occasion to study anatomy in the detail provided by larger, standard text-books. Nurses, physiotherapists and others in allied fields will find this book particularly useful.

JOHN McKENZIE

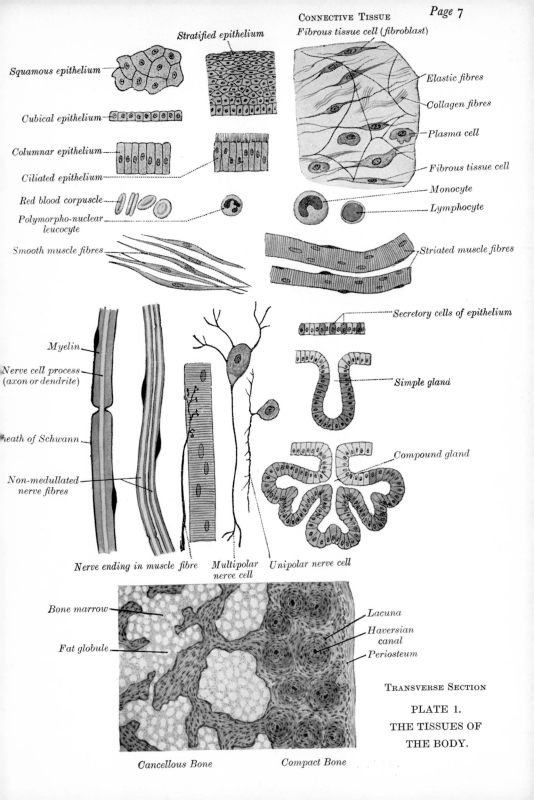

CONNECTIVE TISSUE

Fibrous tissue cell (fibroblast)

Stratified epithelium

Squamous epithelium

Elastic fibres

Collagen fibres

Cubical epithelium

Plasma cell

Columnar epithelium

Ciliated epithelium

Fibrous tissue cell

Red blood corpuscle

Monocyte

Polymorpho-nuclear leucocyte

Lymphocyte

Smooth muscle fibres

Striated muscle fibres

Secretory cells of epithelium

Myelin

Simple gland

Nerve cell process (axon or dendrite)

Sheath of Schwann

Compound gland

Non-medullated nerve fibres

Nerve ending in muscle fibre

Multipolar nerve cell

Unipolar nerve cell

Bone marrow

Lacuna

Haversian canal

Fat globule

Periosteum

TRANSVERSE SECTION

PLATE 1.
THE TISSUES OF
THE BODY.

Cancellous Bone

Compact Bone

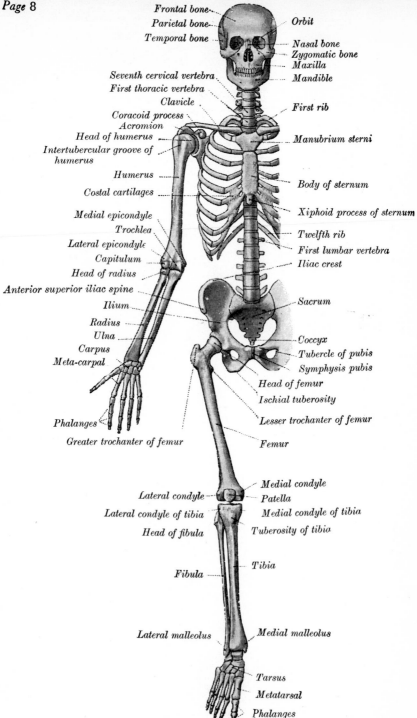

Frontal bone
Parietal bone
Temporal bone
Orbit
Nasal bone
Zygomatic bone
Maxilla
Mandible
Seventh cervical vertebra
First thoracic vertebra
Clavicle
Coracoid process
Acromion
Head of humerus
Intertubercular groove of humerus
Humerus
Costal cartilages
Medial epicondyle
Trochlea
Lateral epicondyle
Capitulum
Head of radius
Anterior superior iliac spine
Ilium
Radius
Ulna
Carpus
Meta-carpal
Phalanges
Greater trochanter of femur
First rib
Manubrium sterni
Body of sternum
Xiphoid process of sternum
Twelfth rib
First lumbar vertebra
Iliac crest
Sacrum
Coccyx
Tubercle of pubis
Symphysis pubis
Head of femur
Ischial tuberosity
Lesser trochanter of femur
Femur
Medial condyle
Patella
Medial condyle of tibia
Tuberosity of tibia
Lateral condyle
Lateral condyle of tibia
Head of fibula
Fibula
Tibia
Lateral malleolus
Medial malleolus
Tarsus
Metatarsal
Phalanges

PLATE 2.—THE HUMAN SKELETON (ANTERIOR VIEW).

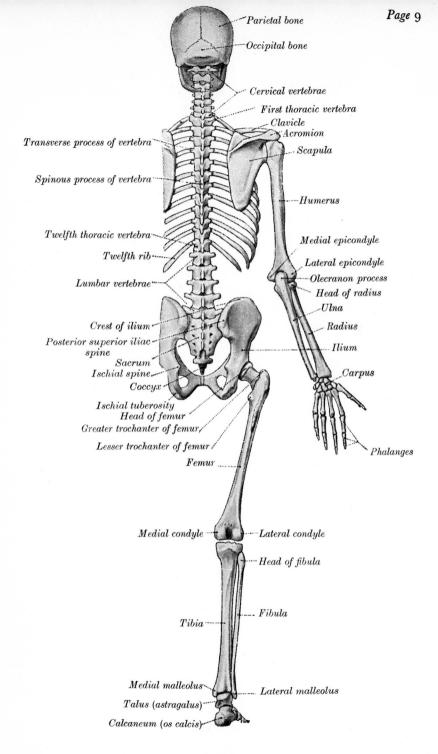

Parietal bone

Occipital bone

Cervical vertebrae

First thoracic vertebra

Clavicle

Acromion

Transverse process of vertebra

Scapula

Spinous process of vertebra

Humerus

Twelfth thoracic vertebra

Medial epicondyle

Twelfth rib

Lateral epicondyle

Olecranon process

Head of radius

Lumbar vertebrae

Ulna

Crest of ilium

Radius

Posterior superior iliac spine

Ilium

Sacrum

Ischial spine

Carpus

Coccyx

Ischial tuberosity

Head of femur

Greater trochanter of femur

Lesser trochanter of femur

Phalanges

Femur

Medial condyle

Lateral condyle

Head of fibula

Fibula

Tibia

Medial malleolus

Lateral malleolus

Talus (astragalus)

Calcaneum (os calcis)

PLATE 3.—THE HUMAN SKELETON (POSTERIOR VIEW).

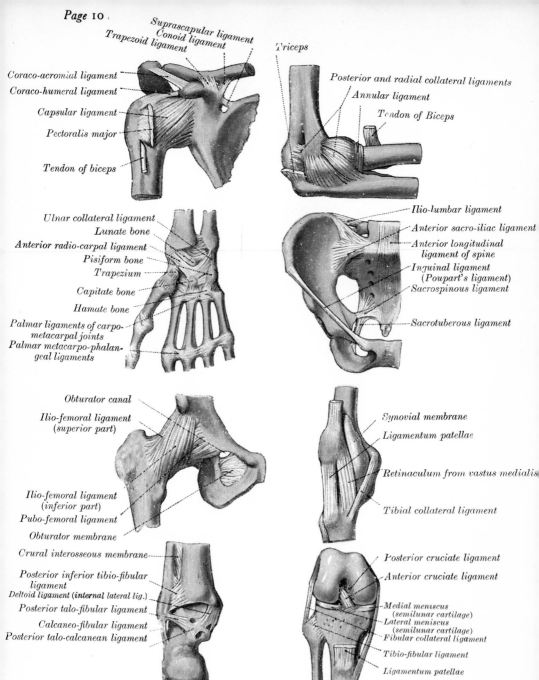

Suprascapular ligament
Conoid ligament
Trapezoid ligament
Coraco-acromial ligament
Coraco-humeral ligament
Capsular ligament
Pectoralis major
Tendon of biceps

Triceps
Posterior and radial collateral ligaments
Annular ligament
Tendon of Biceps

Ulnar collateral ligament
Lunate bone
Anterior radio-carpal ligament
Pisiform bone
Trapezium
Capitate bone
Hamate bone
Palmar ligaments of carpo-metacarpal joints
Palmar metacarpo-phalangeal ligaments

Ilio-lumbar ligament
Anterior sacro-iliac ligament
Anterior longitudinal ligament of spine
Inguinal ligament (Poupart's ligament)
Sacrospinous ligament
Sacrotuberous ligament

Obturator canal
Ilio-femoral ligament (superior part)
Ilio-femoral ligament (inferior part)
Pubo-femoral ligament
Obturator membrane

Synovial membrane
Ligamentum patellae
Retinaculum from vastus medialis
Tibial collateral ligament

Crural interosseous membrane
Posterior inferior tibio-fibular ligament
Deltoid ligament (**internal** lateral lig.)
Posterior talo-fibular ligament
Calcaneo-fibular ligament
Posterior talo-calcanean ligament

Posterior cruciate ligament
Anterior cruciate ligament
Medial meniscus (semilunar cartilage)
Lateral meniscus (semilunar cartilage)
Fibular collateral ligament
Tibio-fibular ligament
Ligamentum patellae

A. K. MAXWELL.

PLATE 4.—JOINTS

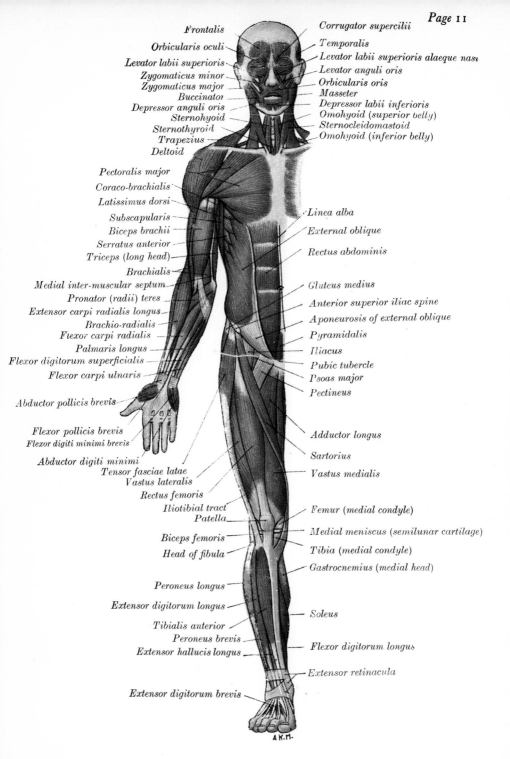

Frontalis
Corrugator supercilii
Orbicularis oculi
Temporalis
Levator labii superioris
Levator labii superioris alaeque nasi
Zygomaticus minor
Levator anguli oris
Zygomaticus major
Orbicularis oris
Buccinator
Masseter
Depressor anguli oris
Depressor labii inferioris
Sternohyoid
Omohyoid (superior belly)
Sternothyroid
Sternocleidomastoid
Trapezius
Omohyoid (inferior belly)
Deltoid

Pectoralis major
Coraco-brachialis
Latissimus dorsi
Linea alba
Subscapularis
External oblique
Biceps brachii
Serratus anterior
Rectus abdominis
Triceps (long head)
Brachialis
Medial inter-muscular septum
Gluteus medius
Pronator (radii) teres
Anterior superior iliac spine
Extensor carpi radialis longus
Aponeurosis of external oblique
Brachio-radialis
Flexor carpi radialis
Pyramidalis
Palmaris longus
Iliacus
Flexor digitorum superficialis
Pubic tubercle
Flexor carpi ulnaris
Psoas major
Pectineus
Abductor pollicis brevis

Flexor pollicis brevis
Flexor digiti minimi brevis
Adductor longus
Abductor digiti minimi
Sartorius
Tensor fasciae latae
Vastus medialis
Vastus lateralis
Rectus femoris
Iliotibial tract
Femur (medial condyle)
Patella
Medial meniscus (semilunar cartilage)
Biceps femoris
Tibia (medial condyle)
Head of fibula
Gastrocnemius (medial head)
Peroneus longus
Extensor digitorum longus
Soleus
Tibialis anterior
Peroneus brevis
Extensor hallucis longus
Flexor digitorum longus
Extensor retinacula
Extensor digitorum brevis

A.K.M.

PLATE 5.—THE MUSCLES OF THE BODY (ANTERIOR VIEW).

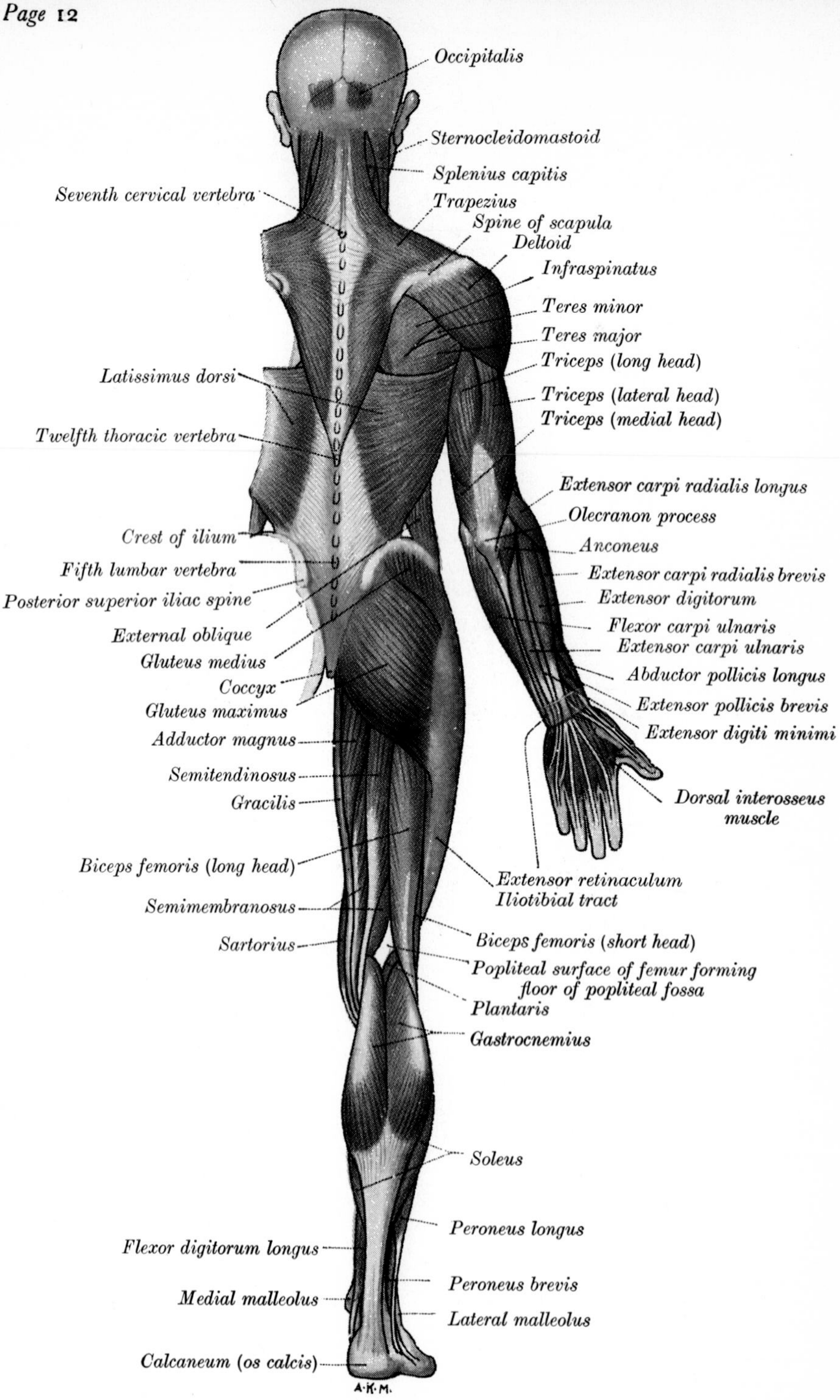

Occipitalis

Sternocleidomastoid

Splenius capitis

Seventh cervical vertebra

Trapezius

Spine of scapula

Deltoid

Infraspinatus

Teres minor

Teres major

Triceps (long head)

Triceps (lateral head)

Triceps (medial head)

Latissimus dorsi

Twelfth thoracic vertebra

Extensor carpi radialis longus

Olecranon process

Crest of ilium

Anconeus

Fifth lumbar vertebra

Extensor carpi radialis brevis

Posterior superior iliac spine

Extensor digitorum

Flexor carpi ulnaris

External oblique

Extensor carpi ulnaris

Gluteus medius

Abductor pollicis longus

Coccyx

Extensor pollicis brevis

Gluteus maximus

Extensor digiti minimi

Adductor magnus

Semitendinosus

Dorsal interosseus muscle

Gracilis

Biceps femoris (long head)

Semimembranosus

Extensor retinaculum

Iliotibial tract

Sartorius

Biceps femoris (short head)

Popliteal surface of femur forming floor of popliteal fossa

Plantaris

Gastrocnemius

Soleus

Peroneus longus

Flexor digitorum longus

Peroneus brevis

Medial malleolus

Lateral malleolus

Calcaneum (os calcis)

A·K·M·

PLATE 6.—THE MUSCLES OF THE BODY (Posterior View).

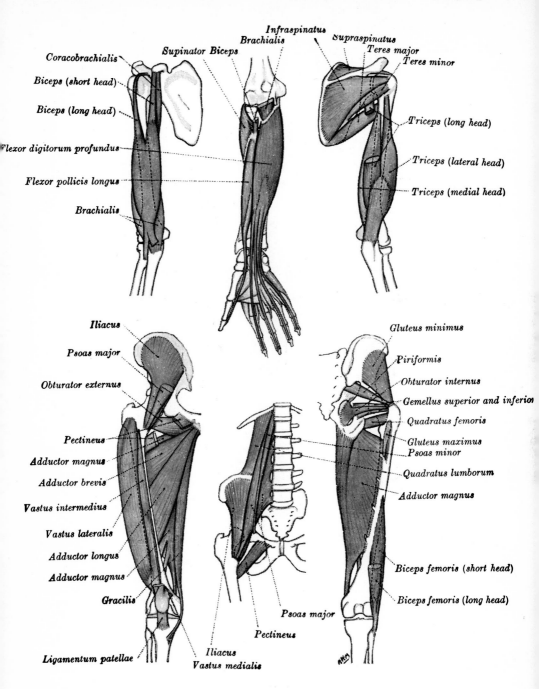

PLATE 7.—DEEP MUSCLES.

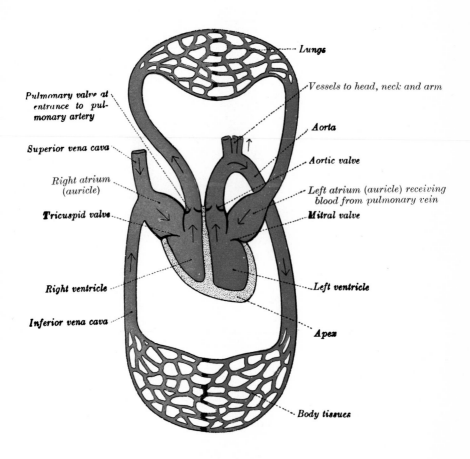

Lungs

Vessels to head, neck and arm

Pulmonary valve at entrance to pulmonary artery

Aorta

Superior vena cava

Aortic valve

Right atrium (auricle)

Left atrium (auricle) receiving blood from pulmonary vein

Tricuspid valve

Mitral valve

Right ventricle

Left ventricle

Inferior vena cava

Apex

Body tissues

PLATE 8.—THE VASCULAR SYSTEM.

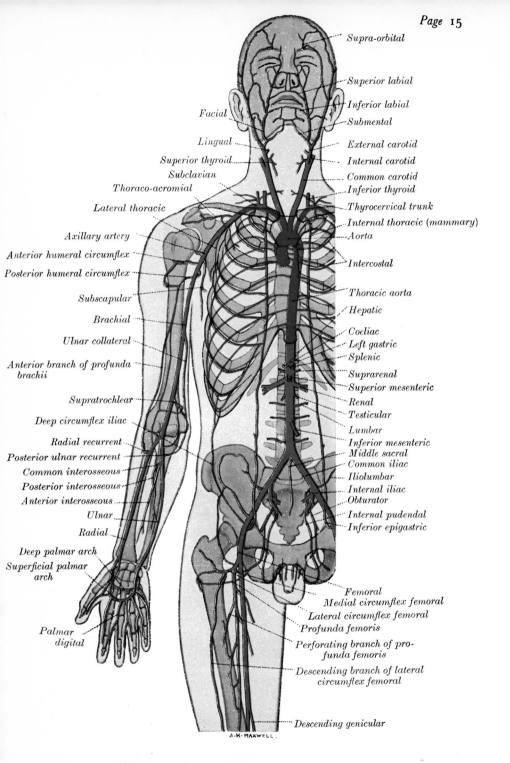

PLATE 9.—THE ARTERIES OF THE BODY

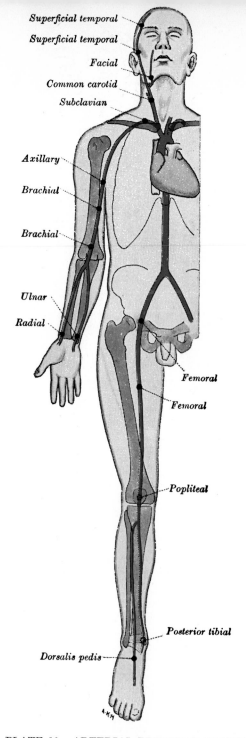

Superficial temporal
Superficial temporal
Facial
Common carotid
Subclavian
Axillary
Brachial
Brachial
Ulnar
Radial
Femoral
Femoral
Popliteal
Posterior tibial
Dorsalis pedis

PLATE 10.—ARTERIAL PRESSURE POINTS

where arteries pass over bone near the surface. Pressure applied over one of these points
will control bleeding from the artery beyond it.

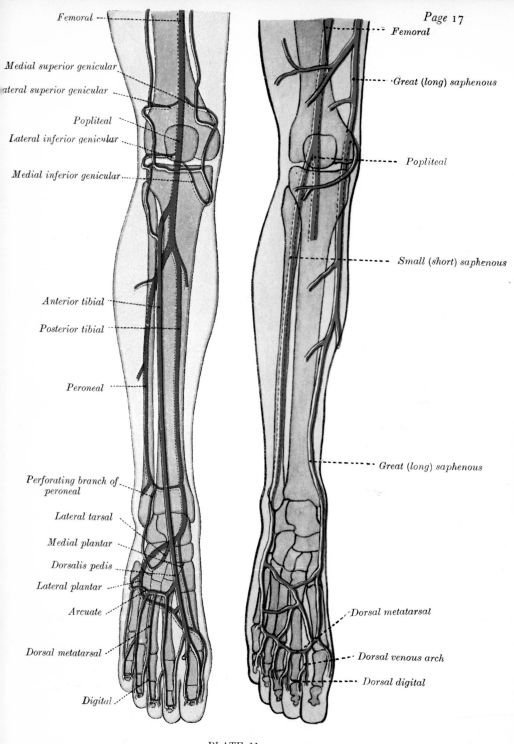

Femoral

Medial superior genicular

ateral superior genicular

Popliteal

Lateral inferior genicular

Medial inferior genicular

Anterior tibial

Posterior tibial

Peroneal

Perforating branch of
peroneal

Lateral tarsal

Medial plantar

Dorsalis pedis

Lateral plantar

Arcuate

Dorsal metatarsal

Digital

Femoral

Great (long) saphenous

Popliteal

Small (short) saphenous

Great (long) saphenous

Dorsal metatarsal

Dorsal venous arch

Dorsal digital

PLATE 11.

ARTERIES OF THE LOWER LIMB.   VEINS OF THE LOWER LIMB

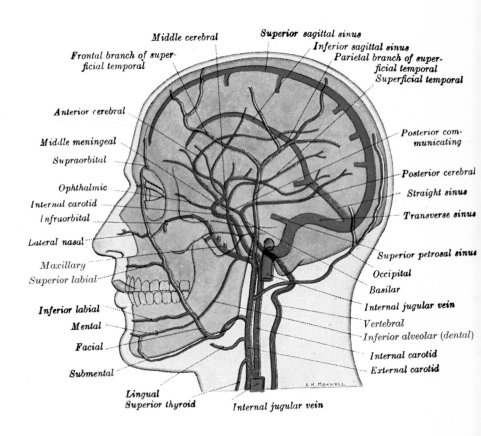

PLATE 12.—THE ARTERIES AND VEINS OF THE HEAD.

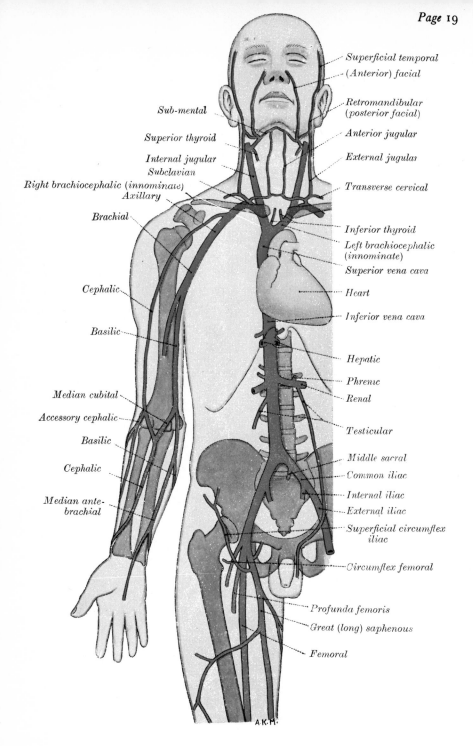

Superficial temporal

(Anterior) facial

Retromandibular
(posterior facial)

Sub-mental

Anterior jugular

Superior thyroid

External jugular

Internal jugular
Subclavian

Transverse cervical

Right brachiocephalic (innominate)
Axillary

Brachial

Inferior thyroid

Left brachiocephalic
(innominate)

Superior vena cava

Cephalic

Heart

Inferior vena cava

Basilic

Hepatic

Phrenic

Median cubital

Renal

Accessory cephalic

Basilic

Testicular

Cephalic

Middle sacral

Common iliac

Internal iliac

Median ante-
brachial

External iliac

Superficial circumflex
iliac

Circumflex femoral

Profunda femoris

Great (long) saphenous

Femoral

A·K·H·

PLATE 13.—THE SYSTEMIC VEINS.

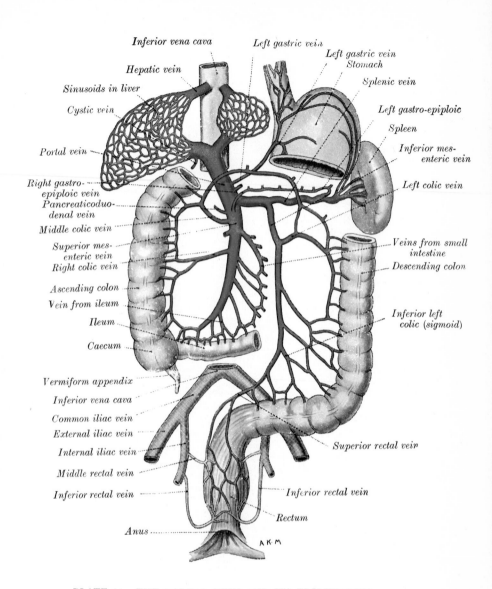

Inferior vena cava

Hepatic vein

Sinusoids in liver

Cystic vein

Portal vein

Right gastro-
epiploic vein
Pancreaticoduo-
denal vein
Middle colic vein

Superior mes-
enteric vein
Right colic vein

Ascending colon

Vein from ileum

Ileum

Caecum

Vermiform appendix

Inferior vena cava

Common iliac vein

External iliac vein

Internal iliac vein

Middle rectal vein

Inferior rectal vein

Anus

Left gastric vein

Left gastric vein
Stomach

Splenic vein

Left gastro-epiploic

Spleen

Inferior mes-
enteric vein

Left colic vein

Veins from small
intestine

Descending colon

Inferior left
colic (sigmoid)

Superior rectal vein

Inferior rectal vein

Rectum

A K M

PLATE 14.—THE PORTAL VEIN AND ITS TRIBUTARIES.

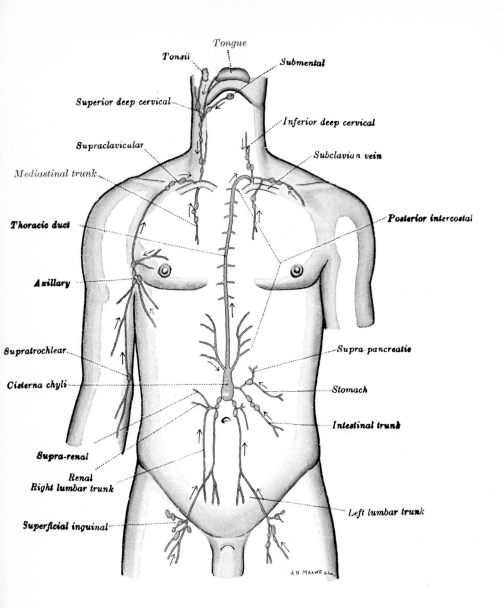

PLATE 15.— THE LYMPHATIC SYSTEM.

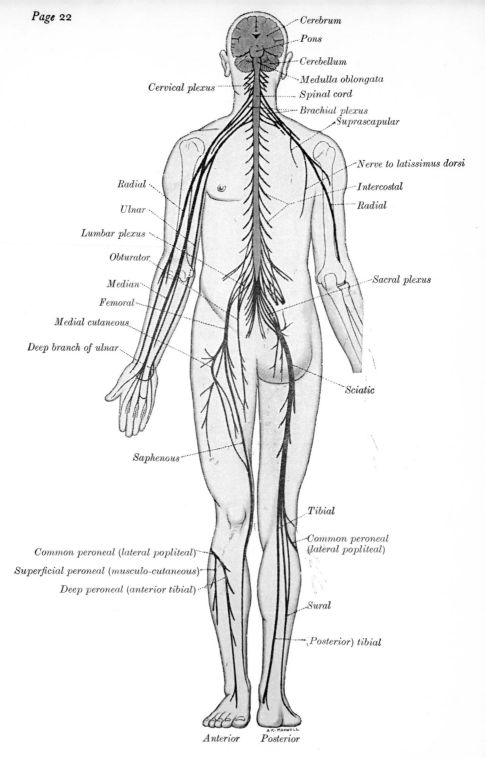

Cerebrum

Pons

Cerebellum

Medulla oblongata

Cervical plexus

Spinal cord

Brachial plexus

Suprascapular

Nerve to latissimus dorsi

Radial

Intercostal

Ulnar

Radial

Lumbar plexus

Obturator

Median

Sacral plexus

Femoral

Medial cutaneous

Deep branch of ulnar

Sciatic

Saphenous

Tibial

Common peroneal (lateral popliteal)

Superficial peroneal (musculo-cutaneous)

Common peroneal (lateral popliteal)

Deep peroneal (anterior tibial)

Sural

(Posterior) tibial

Anterior   Posterior

PLATE 16.—THE CENTRAL NERVOUS SYSTEM AND PERIPHERAL NERVES.

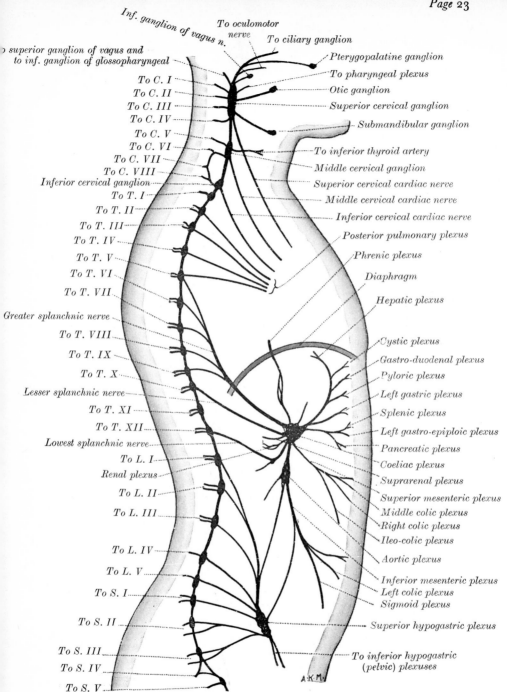

Inf. ganglion of vagus n.
To oculomotor nerve
To ciliary ganglion

superior ganglion of vagus and to inf. ganglion of glossopharyngeal

Pterygopalatine ganglion
To pharyngeal plexus
Otic ganglion
Superior cervical ganglion
Submandibular ganglion

To C. I
To C. II
To C. III
To C. IV
To C. V
To C. VI
To C. VII
To C. VIII
Inferior cervical ganglion
To T. I
To T. II
To T. III
To T. IV
To T. V
To T. VI
To T. VII
Greater splanchnic nerve
To T. VIII
To T. IX
To T. X
Lesser splanchnic nerve
To T. XI
To T. XII
Lowest splanchnic nerve
To L. I
Renal plexus
To L. II
To L. III
To L. IV
To L. V
To S. I
To S. II
To S. III
To S. IV
To S. V

To inferior thyroid artery
Middle cervical ganglion
Superior cervical cardiac nerve
Middle cervical cardiac nerve
Inferior cervical cardiac nerve
Posterior pulmonary plexus
Phrenic plexus
Diaphragm
Hepatic plexus
Cystic plexus
Gastro-duodenal plexus
Pyloric plexus
Left gastric plexus
Splenic plexus
Left gastro-epiploic plexus
Pancreatic plexus
Coeliac plexus
Suprarenal plexus
Superior mesenteric plexus
Middle colic plexus
Right colic plexus
Ileo-colic plexus
Aortic plexus
Inferior mesenteric plexus
Left colic plexus
Sigmoid plexus
Superior hypogastric plexus
To inferior hypogastric (pelvic) plexuses

A.K.M.

PLATE 17.—THE SYMPATHETIC SYSTEM.

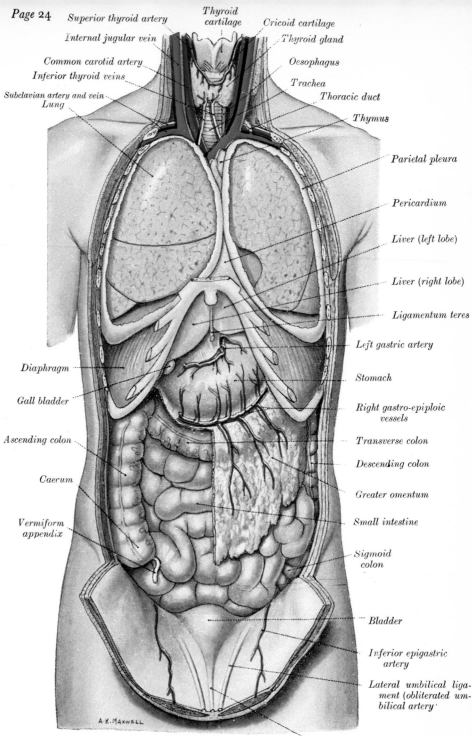

Superior thyroid artery — Thyroid cartilage — Cricoid cartilage
Internal jugular vein — Thyroid gland
Common carotid artery — Oesophagus
Inferior thyroid veins — Trachea
Subclavian artery and vein — Thoracic duct
Lung — Thymus

Parietal pleura

Pericardium

Liver (left lobe)

Liver (right lobe)

Ligamentum teres

Left gastric artery

Stomach

Right gastro-epiploic vessels

Transverse colon

Descending colon

Greater omentum

Small intestine

Sigmoid colon

Bladder

Inferior epigastric artery

Lateral umbilical ligament (obliterated umbilical artery)

Diaphragm

Gall bladder

Ascending colon

Caecum

Vermiform appendix

Median umbilical ligament (urachus)

A·K·MAXWELL

PLATE 18.—THE THORAX AND ABDOMEN (1).

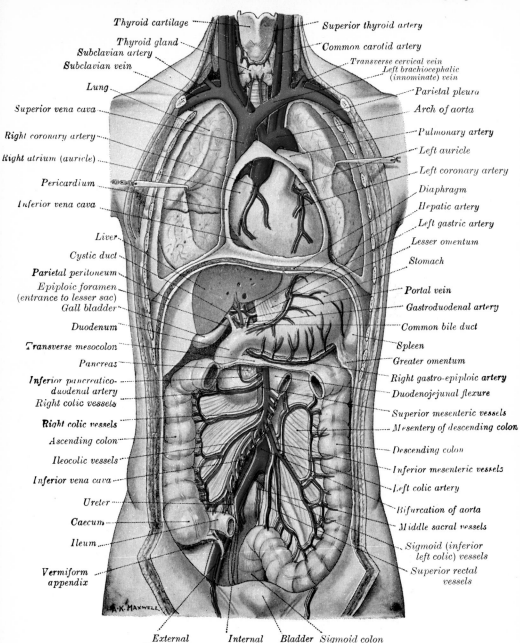

Thyroid cartilage

Thyroid gland

Subclavian artery

Subclavian vein

Lung

Superior vena cava

Right coronary artery

Right atrium (auricle)

Pericardium

Inferior vena cava

Liver

Cystic duct

Parietal peritoneum

Epiploic foramen
(entrance to lesser sac)

Gall bladder

Duodenum

Transverse mesocolon

Pancreas

Inferior pancreatico-
duodenal artery

Right colic vessels

Right colic vessels

Ascending colon

Ileocolic vessels

Inferior vena cava

Ureter

Caecum

Ileum

Vermiform
appendix

Superior thyroid artery

Common carotid artery

Transverse cervical vein
Left brachiocephalic
(innominate) vein

Parietal pleura

Arch of aorta

Pulmonary artery

Left auricle

Left coronary artery

Diaphragm

Hepatic artery

Left gastric artery

Lesser omentum

Stomach

Portal vein

Gastroduodenal artery

Common bile duct

Spleen

Greater omentum

Right gastro-epiploic artery

Duodenojejunal flexure

Superior mesenteric vessels

Mesentery of descending colon

Descending colon

Inferior mesenteric vessels

Left colic artery

Bifurcation of aorta

Middle sacral vessels

Sigmoid (inferior
left colic) vessels

Superior rectal
vessels

A.K. MAXWELL

External
iliac vessels

Internal
iliac vessels

Bladder

Sigmoid colon

PLATE 19.—THE THORAX AND ABDOMEN (2)

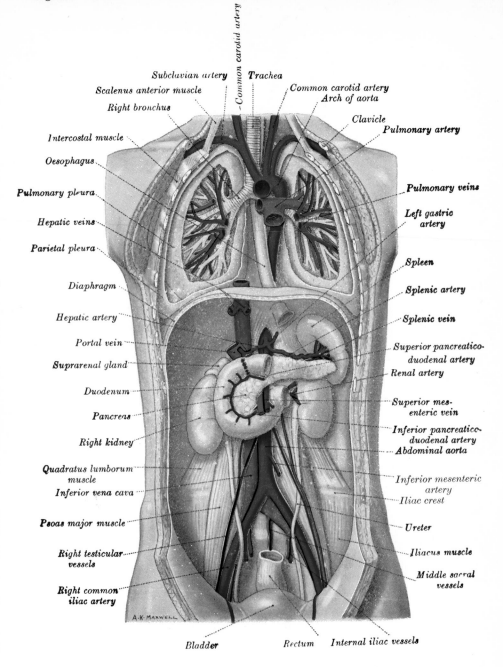

PLATE 20.—THE THORAX AND ABDOMEN (3).

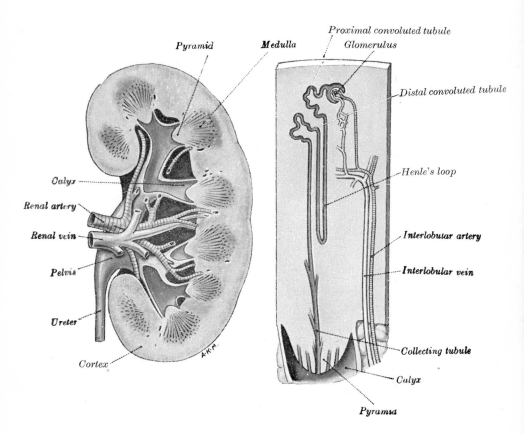

VERTICAL SECTION THROUGH
A KIDNEY.

SCHEME OF A NEPHRON AND
ITS VASCULAR SUPPLY

PLATE 21

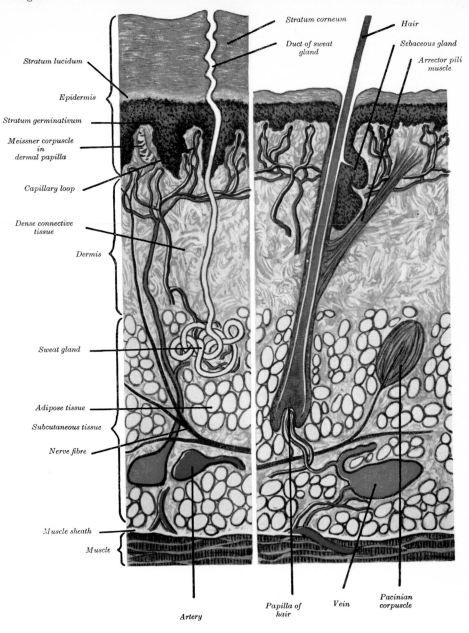

Stratum corneum

Hair

Duct of sweat
gland

Sebaceous gland

Arrector pili
muscle

Stratum lucidum

Epidermis

Stratum germinativum

Meissner corpuscle
in
dermal papilla

Capillary loop

Dense connective
tissue

Dermis

Sweat gland

Adipose tissue

Subcutaneous tissue

Nerve fibre

Muscle sheath

Muscle

Papilla of
hair

Vein

Pacinian
corpuscle

Artery

(1)   (2)

PLATE 22.—(1) A SECTION THROUGH THE SKIN OF THE PALM.
(2) A SECTION THROUGH THE SKIN OF THE TRUNK.

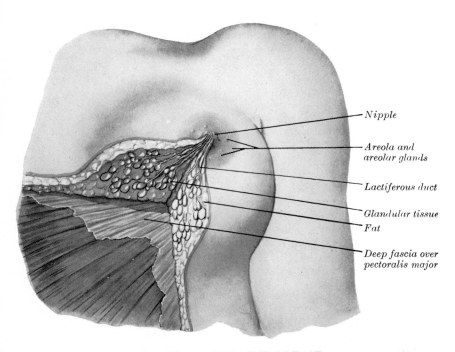

Nipple

Areola and
areolar glands

Lactiferous duct

Glandular tissue

Fat

Deep fascia over
pectoralis major

PLATE 23.—THE LEFT BREAST

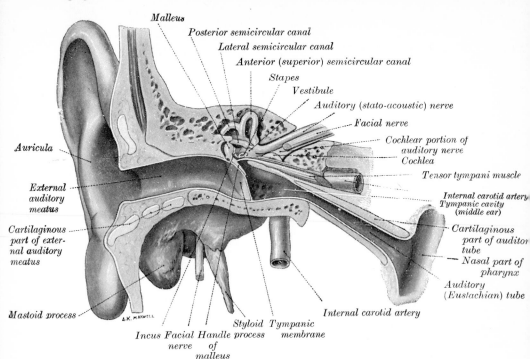

PLATE 24.—EXTERNAL, MIDDLE AND INTERNAL PORTIONS OF THE
RIGHT EAR FROM THE FRONT.

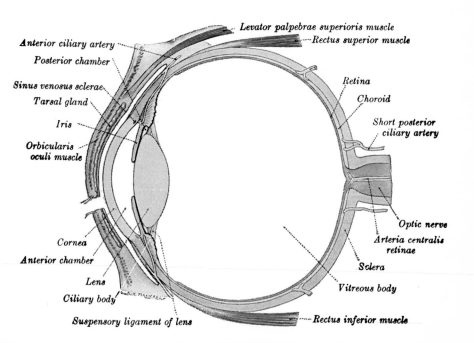

PLATE 25.—A SAGITTAL SECTION THROUGH THE EYE

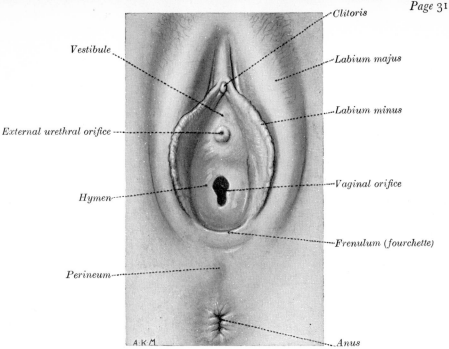

PLATE 26.—THE EXTERNAL GENITAL ORGANS OF THE FEMALE

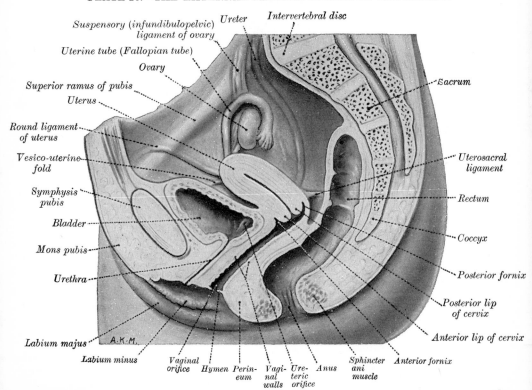

PLATE 27.—A MEDIAN SAGITTAL SECTION THROUGH THE FEMALE PELVIS

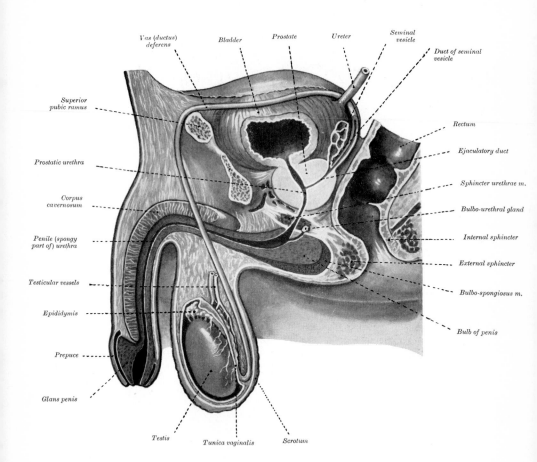

Vas (ductus) deferens — Bladder — Prostate — Ureter — Seminal vesicle — Duct of seminal vesicle — Superior pubic ramus — Rectum — Ejaculatory duct — Prostatic urethra — Sphincter urethrae m. — Corpus cavernosum — Bulbo-urethral gland — Penile (spongy part of) urethra — Internal sphincter — Testicular vessels — External sphincter — Epididymis — Bulbo-spongiosus m. — Prepuce — Bulb of penis — Glans penis — Testis — Tunica vaginalis — Scrotum

PLATE 28.—MALE GENITAL ORGANS

ELEMENTARY HISTOLOGY

EVERY living structure is composed of *cells* and *intercellular material*. Much of the intercellular material acts as a cement between the cells but some of it provides strength, for example, collagen and elastic fibres in the skin and calcium salts in bone. Each cell is a microscopic portion of *protoplasm* within which is a denser part, the *nucleus*. Within the nucleus is the *nucleolus*. Cells and intercellular material combine to form *tissues*; tissues form *organs* and organs form *systems*.

Tissues can be classified as:

Solid Tissues	Fluid Tissues
Epithelium.	Blood (page 41).
Connective tissue.	Lymph (page 42).
Muscle tissue (page 37).	Cerebro-spinal fluid (page 44).
Nerve tissue (page 43).	

Epithelium is found:

(i) Covering the exterior of the body.

(ii) Lining all internal cavities such as the alimentary, respiratory, and genito-urinary tracts.

(iii) Lining all blood and lymph vessels, where it is sometimes called endothelium.

(iv) Forming all glands and lining their ducts.

1. Simple epithelium consists of one layer of cells.

2. Stratified (compound) epithelium consists of two or more layers.

1. Simple epithelia (Fig. 1):

(i) *Squamous* or *pavement:* lines blood and lymph vessels, air sacs of lungs, etc.

(ii) *Cubical:* lines the ducts of glands such as the salivary glands and liver; also the ducts of the kidney tubules.

(iii) *Ciliated:* lines the respiratory tract (except the pharynx), middle ear, auditory tube, uterine tubes, etc.

(iv) *Secretory* or *glandular cells* are arranged round a central lumen or hollow into which secretion is poured.

2. Stratified epithelia:

(i) *Stratified squamous:* forms the upper layers of the skin, lines the mouth, pharynx, and the oesophagus.

(ii) *Transitional:* a type of stratified epithelium lining the bladder and urethra.

Epithelium with a backing of connective tissue forms *membranes* (page 48).

Connective tissue (Fig. 1) connects all other tissues and in the form of bone gives rigidity and support. Different types include:

(i) *Areolar* or *loose connective tissue* surrounds all vessels, nerves, and muscle fibres.

(ii) *Adipose tissue* (fat) is distributed under the skin, behind the eyes and around the kidneys.

(iii) *Lymphoid, adenoid* or *reticular* tissue forms the tonsils, lymph nodes, and the spleen.

(iv) *Dense connective tissue* forms strong bands such as ligaments and tendons.

C

(v) *Yellow elastic tissue* is found where elasticity is essential, such as in the walls of blood vessels.

(vi) *Cartilage* or gristle is a semi-rigid substance of three types:

     (*a*) *White fibro-cartilage* found in joints of limited movement, e.g. intervertebral.

     (*b*) *Yellow elastic cartilage* found in the epiglottis and pinna.

     (*c*) *Hyaline cartilage* found in the costal cartilages.

(vii) *Bone* forms the skeleton. *Dense* or *compact bone* (Fig. 1) is composed of closely packed *Haversian systems*, i.e. concentric layers of bone surrounding a central *Haversian canal* carrying blood vessels to nourish the bone. Surrounding these Haversian canals between the layers of bone are concentric rings of *lacunae* containing the bone cells (*osteocytes*). Minute channels, the *canaliculi*, link up the lacunae with each other and with the Haversian canals. Thus food, oxygen, etc., pass from the blood vessels in the Haversian canals along the canaliculi to nourish the bone cells in their lacunae. *Cancellous bone* (Fig. 1) consists of a spongework of bony struts or strands, the intervening spaces filled with blood vessels and bone marrow.

Bones are classified as:

    (i) *Long bones*, e.g. the humerus and femur.

    (ii) *Short bones*, e.g. the metatarsal bones.

    (iii) *Flat bones*, e.g. the frontal and occipital bones.

    (iv) *Irregular bones*, e.g. the vertebrae and sphenoid.

    (v) *Sesamoid bones* which develop in the tendons of certain muscles, e.g. the patella.

The Structure of a Long Bone.

It consists of a shaft or *diaphysis* and two ends or *epiphyses*. The *medullary cavity* which passes through the shaft is filled with yellow bone marrow consisting largely of fat. The ends consist of a thin outer layer (*cortex*) of dense bone enclosing cancellous bone. The shaft of the bone, possessing a much thicker cortex, is covered with *periosteum* (Fig. 1), an important membrane protecting and controlling the configuration of the bone by means of an innermost layer of cells, the *osteoblasts*, a middle vascular layer for the nutrition of the bone and an outer fibrous layer.

Long bone grows in thickness from the inner layer of the periosteum. It grows in length from the *epiphyseal cartilages*, which in youth separate the ends from the shaft. These cartilages become ossified in adolescence and growth of bone, in a longitudinal direction, ceases.

THE SKELETON

(Figs. 2 and 3)

22 Bones form the Skull:

8 Bones of the Cranium:

     1 *frontal* bone forms the forehead;

     2 *parietal* bones form the top and sides of the cranium;

1 *occipital* bone posteriorly;

2 *temporal* bones assist in forming the sides of the cranium;

1 *sphenoid* bone forms the greater part of the base of the skull;

1 *ethmoid* bone also in the base of the skull lies in front of the sphenoid.

14 Bones of the Face:

2 *maxillae* form the upper jaw and most of the hard palate;

1 *mandible* forms the lower jaw;

2 *zygomatic* (*malar*) or cheek bones;

2 *nasal bones* form the bridge of the nose;

1 *vomer* divides the cavity of the nose into two compartments;

2 *lacrimal* bones, in the orbits, with the naso-lacrimal ducts lying against them;

2 *palatine* bones, each L-shaped, the horizontal part in the roof of the mouth, the vertical part in the side wall of the nose;

2 *inferior nasal conchae* lie in the lateral walls of the nose.

1 Hyoid Bone lies in the upper portion of the neck anteriorly and is detached from the skeleton.

33 Bones form the Spine:

24 *true vertebrae* are separated by pads of fibro-cartilage, the *intervertebral discs*, which allow of some movement between them. These are:

    (i)   7 *cervical* vertebrae; the 1st cervical vertebra is called the *atlas*, the second the *axis*;

    (ii) 12 *thoracic* or *dorsal* vertebrae;

    (iii) 5 *lumbar* vertebrae.

9 *false vertebrae* are closely fused together so that there is no movement between them:

    (iv) 5 *sacral* vertebrae;

    (v) 4 *coccygeal* vertebrae.

25 Bones form the Chest or Thorax:

12 pairs of ribs form the sides of the chest;

    True ribs, the first 7 pairs; each is joined to the sternum by its own costal cartilage.

    False ribs, the last 5 pairs, are not so joined to the sternum.

    The 8th, 9th and 10th pairs are joined by costal cartilages to the cartilages of the 7th pair. The 11th and 12th pairs or *floating ribs* are unattached anteriorly.

12 dorsal vertebrae lie posteriorly.

1 *sternum*, or breast bone, lies in the middle line anteriorly. It consists of:

    (*a*) the *manubrium*, the proximal end;

    (*b*) the *body*, the central portion;

    (*c*) the *ensiform* or *xiphoid process*, the distal portion.

4 Bones form the Shoulder Girdles:

2 *clavicles* or collar bones;

2 *scapulae* or shoulder blades.

60 Bones form the Upper Limbs, in each:

  1 *humerus* of the upper arm;
  1 *radius*, the outer bone of the forearm;
  1 *ulna*, the inner bone of the forearm;
  8 *carpal* bones of the wrist:

    scaphoid, lunate, triquetral, pisiform, trapezium, trapezoid, capitate, and *hamate.*

  5 *metacarpal* bones of the hand;
  14 *phalanges* or finger bones.

4 Bones form the Pelvis:

  Right and left *hip* (*innominate*) bones form the front and sides. Each innominate bone consists of:
    the *ilium* above,
    the *ischium* posteriorly,
    and the *pubis* anteriorly.
  Sacrum ⎫
  Coccyx ⎭ posteriorly.

60 Bones form the Lower Limbs, in each:

  1 *femur* or thigh bone;
  1 *tibia*, the inner bone of the leg;
  1 *fibula*, the outer (splint) bone of the leg;
  1 *patella* or knee cap;
  7 *tarsal* bones of the ankle:
    the *calcaneum* or os calcis, the heel bone,
    the *talus* or astragalus, the ankle bone,
    the *navicular* or scaphoid, on the inner border of the foot,
    the *cuboid* on the outer border of the foot,
    the *lateral cuneiform,*
    the *intermediate cuneiform,*
    the *medial cuneiform.*
  5 *metatarsal* bones of the foot;
  14 *phalanges* form the toes.

For the most important foramina, prominences, etc., see Figs. 2 and 3.

JOINTS

Joints are formed where bones articulate with one another (Fig. 4).

1. **Joints** which allow little or no movement.
  (*a*) *Fixed joints* allow no movement between the bones; e.g. the *sutures* of the skull.
  (*b*) *Mixed joints* allow limited movement; e.g. the joints between the true vertebrae.

2. **Joints** which allow free movement, usually called *synovial* joints.
  (*a*) *Ball and socket joints:* e.g. the hip and shoulder joints.
  (*b*) *Hinge joints:* e.g. the knee and elbow joints.

(c) *Pivot joints:* e.g. the superior radio-ulnar joint and the atlanto-axial joint.
(d) *Gliding joints:* e.g. the carpal and tarsal joints.
The structures forming all synovial joints are:

(a) Bones, two or more, which are generally enlarged at their articular surfaces.
(b) Cartilage covers the articular surfaces. Other cartilages may be present, such as the *menisci* or semi-lunar cartilages of the knee joint.
(c) Ligaments are strong bands of fibrous tissue passing between the bones.
(d) Synovial membrane, which secretes synovial fluid to lubricate the joints. This membrane lines joint cavities and in certain joints forms *bursae* (sacs).

THE MUSCULAR SYSTEM
(Figs. 5 and 6)

Muscle consists of elongated muscle cells or fibres which contract in response to stimuli. Muscle contraction produces movement and heat.

1. **Striated, Voluntary or Skeletal Muscle** (Fig. 1) consists of cylindrical fibres which are red because they contain muscle haemoglobin (myoglobin); the fibres are faintly striated or cross-banded, and movement is under control of the will. These muscles cover the skeleton. Voluntary muscles are encased in *connective tissue* which is prolonged beyond the ends of the muscles and strengthened to form *tendons* or *aponeuroses* (flat tendons) by which the muscles are attached to other structures such as bone.

The names and positions of the principal voluntary muscles will be found on Figs. 5, 6 and 7.

2. **Smooth, Involuntary or Plain Muscle** consists of short spindle-shaped fibres showing no cross-striations; their movement is not under control of the will. This type is found in the walls of viscera, like the stomach, intestines, bladder and uterus.

3. **Cardiac Muscle** is found only in the heart. The fibres, branching and anastomosing with each other, are not wholly dependent on nerve stimulus and can initiate their own contractions.

THE CARDIO-VASCULAR SYSTEM

The Cardio-Vascular or Circulatory System comprises the heart and blood vessels.

The Heart is a hollow cone-shaped muscular organ occupying the greater part of the mediastinum. It measures about 5″ long × 3½″ across. The base is directed upwards, backwards, and to the right; the apex downwards, forwards, and to the left. The apex beat is felt usually in the fifth intercostal space, 3½″ to the left of the middle line.

Pericardium (Figs. 18 and 19) is a double serous membrane surrounding the heart. The *visceral* or inner layer is adherent to the heart muscle; the *parietal* or outer layer fuses, above, with the great vessels of the heart and, below, with the diaphragm.

Myocardium, the heart muscle, is thicker on the left side than on the right.

Endocardium is smooth endothelium lining the heart.

The *septum* (Fig. 8) separates the R. and L. sides of the heart, allowing of no direct communication after birth. The heart is further divided into 4 chambers, the R. and L. *atria* above, and the R. and L. *ventricles* (Figs. 8, 18, 19) below.

The *tricuspid valve* (Fig. 8) separates the R. atrium from the R. ventricle. The *bicuspid* or *mitral valve* separates the L. atrium from the L. ventricle.

The *chordae tendineae* are fibrous cords which connect the valves with the papillary muscles of the ventricles. The *aortic valve* (Fig. 8) lies where the aorta leaves the L. ventricle, the *pulmonary valve* where the pulmonary artery leaves the R. ventricle. The *sinu-atrial*, or *S.A. node*, the 'pace-maker' of the heart, is a little collection of specialised cells situated in the R. atrial wall near the entrance of the superior vena cava. There the stimuli for the heart's contraction originate and spread throughout the walls of both atria. The *atrioventricular* (A.-V.) *node*, consisting of specialised conducting tissue and lying in the inter-atrial septum just above the tricuspid valve, picks up the contraction impulses from the atrial muscle and transmits them via the *atrioventricular bundle (of His)* and the *subendocardial network* to the muscle of the ventricles. Thus each contraction of the atria is followed almost immediately by contraction of both ventricles.

BLOOD VESSELS

The walls of all larger blood vessels consist of three coats or tunics:

Tunica adventitia, the outer coat, which is tough and fibrous.

Tunica media, the middle coat, consists of smooth muscle and elastic tissue.

Tunica intima, the inner coat, is a smooth endothelium.

Arteries: all convey blood *away* from the heart. With the exception of the pulmonary arteries all carry oxygenated blood. Arteries branch to form—

Arterioles (small arteries). Arteriole walls have less fibrous and elastic and more muscle tissue, allowing more ready contraction and relaxation. Arterioles subdivide to form—

Capillaries, the smallest blood vessels. Their walls consist of a single layer of permeable endothelium. Capillaries anastomose with

Venules or small veins, which in turn join to form

Veins. All veins convey blood *towards* the heart. With the exception of the pulmonary veins, all carry de-oxygenated blood. Their walls have more fibrous tissue and less elastic and muscular tissue than arteries. The veins of the limbs are supplied with *valves* which allow the blood to flow towards the heart but prevent it flowing backwards where the pressure is least and the flow is against gravity.

Blood vessel walls are supplied by *vaso-motor nerves* of two types:

(a) *Vaso-constrictors*, which on stimulation constrict vessels and raise the blood pressure.

(b) *Vaso-dilators*, which on stimulation relax the vessels and lower the blood pressure.

CIRCULATION

Circulation can be divided into:

1. **Coronary Circulation** through the heart muscle. Blood passes from the L. ventricle to the aorta, thence to the R. and L. coronary arteries (Fig. 19), through the heart muscle, and back by the cardiac veins and coronary sinus to the R. atrium.

2. **Pulmonary Circulation** (Fig. 8) by which blood is oxygenated. Blood passes from the R. atrium to the R. ventricle, thence to the pulmonary artery and so to the lungs, returning by the pulmonary veins to the L. atrium.

3. **Portal Circulation** (Fig. 14) from the digestive organs and spleen to the liver.

Superior mesenteric vein drains the small intestine and part of the large intestine.
Inferior mesenteric vein drains the rest of the large intestine.
Gastric veins drain the stomach.
Splenic vein drains the spleen.
All drain into the *portal vein* which passes into the liver.

4. **Systemic Circulation** (Figs. 9, 10, 11, 12, 13) is the circulation throughout the body. Blood enters the L. ventricle from the L. atrium and leaves by the aorta, which sends branches to all parts of the body.

A. Ascending Aorta (Figs. 8, 9) gives off the R. and L. *coronary arteries* to the heart muscle.

B. Arch of Aorta (Figs. 8, 9, 10, 19) gives off 3 large vessels to the neck, head, and upper limbs:

    (i) *Brachiocephalic (innominate) artery*, to the right, bifurcates to form
        (a) the *R. common carotid artery* to the right side of head and neck.
        (b) the *R. subclavian artery* to the right upper limb.
    (ii) the *L. common carotid artery* to the left side of the head and neck.
   (iii) the *L. subclavian artery* to the left upper limb.

C. Thoracic Aorta supplies the thoracic viscera. Its branches include:

    (i) Bronchial arteries (3) to the lungs and the bronchi.
   (ii) Pericardial arteries to the pericardium.
  (iii) Oesophageal arteries (4 or 5) to the oesophagus.
  (iv) Intercostal arteries (9 pairs) to the intercostal muscles (Fig. 9).

D. Abdominal Aorta supplies the abdominal viscera:

    (i) *Phrenic arteries* (2) to the diaphragm,
   (ii) *Coeliac axis* (Figs. 9, 20) branches to give off
        (a) *Hepatic artery* to the liver (Fig. 20).
        (b) *L. gastric artery* to the stomach (Figs. 18, 19, 20).
        (c) *Splenic artery* to the spleen (Fig. 20). The splenic artery sends branches to the pancreas.
  (iii) *Supra-renal arteries* (2) to the supra-renal glands.
  (iv) *Superior mesenteric artery* (Fig. 19) to the small intestine; it also sends branches to the large intestine.
   (v) *Renal arteries* (2) to the kidneys (Fig. 20).
  (vi) *Testicular arteries* (Fig. 20) to the spermatic cords and testes (male), *Ovarian arteries* (2) to the ovaries (female).

(vii) *Inf. mesenteric artery* (Fig. 20) to the large intestine. It continues as the *superior rectal (or haemorrhoidal) artery* to the rectum.

(viii) *Lumbar arteries* (5 pairs) to the lumbar muscles and abdominal wall.

(ix) *Median sacral artery* to the sacrum.

At the level of the 4th lumbar vertebra, the aorta bifurcates to form

(x) *R.* and *L. common iliac arteries.*

The common iliac arteries (Fig. 9) in turn bifurcate to form the ext. and int. iliac arteries.

Int. iliac arteries supply the pelvic viscera. Their branches include:

Vesical arteries to the bladder;

middle rectal (or haemorrhoidal) arteries to the rectum;

uterine arteries to the uterus;

vaginal arteries to the vagina.

Ext. iliac arteries pass downwards and outwards to supply the lower limbs. Their course and branches can be traced on Figs. 9 and 11.

The Venous Return from the Limbs can be traced on Figs. 11 and 13.

Arterial Flow to Face and Scalp (Figs. 9 and 12). The *L. common carotid* artery from the aorta and the *R. common carotid* artery from the brachiocephalic artery pass upwards on each side of the neck. Opposite the upper border of the thyroid cartilage they divide to form the *ext.* and *int. carotid* arteries. Ext. carotid arteries pass upwards and outwards. They give off:

superior thyroid arteries to the thyroid gland;

lingual arteries to the tongue;

facial arteries which ascend over the mandible on to the face, giving off the ascending palatine, tonsillar, submandibular, submental, inferior labial, and lateral nasal arteries;

occipital arteries which give off the mastoid and small meningeal arteries (the latter passing through the jugular foramina); *posterior auricular* arteries to the ears; *ascending pharyngeal* arteries to the pharynx, soft palate and the tonsils. In front of the ears, the external carotid arteries divide to form the *superficial temporal* arteries and the *maxillary* arteries. The latter give off the *middle meningeal* arteries and the *small meningeal* arteries and supply the teeth of the upper and lower jaw.

Venous Return Flow from Face and Scalp. The principal veins accompany the arteries and bear the same names. These veins drain into the *ext. jugular veins* (Fig. 13) which open into subclavian veins or into the *int. jugular veins.*

Arterial Flow to Brain (Fig. 12) is principally by 2 pairs of arteries:

R. and *L. vertebral arteries* arise from the subclavian arteries;

R. and *L. internal carotid arteries* arise from the common carotid arteries.

R. and L. vertebral arteries pass up through foramina in the transverse processes of the cervical vertebrae, through the foramen magnum and so into the skull, where they join to form the *basilar artery.* The basilar artery gives off the *anterior inferior cerebellar* and *superior cerebellar* arteries and divides into the *posterior cerebral arteries.*

The R. and L. internal carotid arteries pass through the carotid canals of the temporal bone into the skull; each gives off the *ophthalmic artery* and divides into *anterior* and *middle cerebral arteries.*

With the basilar artery, the internal carotid arteries form an *arterial circle* (*of Willis*) at the base of the brain in the following manner: each posterior cerebral artery (from the basilar) is linked to the middle cerebral artery (from the internal carotid) by a *posterior communicating artery* and the two anterior cerebral arteries are joined by the *anterior communicating artery*.

Venous Return Flow from Brain (Fig. 12). Venous blood passes into *sinuses*, which lie between the layers of the dura mater. The *superior sagittal sinus* passes along the roof of the skull from back to front. It drains into the R. transverse sinus. The *inferior longitudinal sinus* lies deeply and drains into the *straight sinus* which in turn opens into the L. transverse sinus. *R.* and *L. transverse sinuses* lie above and behind the middle ears. They open into the *internal jugular veins* which pass down the neck, joining the subclavian veins to form the *brachiocephalic veins*. These, in turn, unite to form the *superior vena cava*.

All venous blood passes into the R. atrium by
  (*a*) the *superior vena cava* draining the head, neck, chest and upper limbs;
  (*b*) the *inferior vena cava* draining the lower limbs, pelvis and abdomen;
  (*c*) the *coronary sinus* draining the heart muscle.

BLOOD

Blood has a specific gravity of 1059, is alkaline in reaction and amounts to approximately 6 litres (11 pints) in the average adult. It consists of *plasma* and the blood cells, *red corpuscles, white corpuscles* and *platelets*.

Plasma is a clear, straw-coloured fluid holding various substances in solution. These include: sugar, 100–120 mgms. per 100 c.cs. of blood; urea, 20–40 mgms. per 100 c.cs.; amino acids, fats, mineral salts, gases, and enzymes. Plasma exudes through the capillary walls to bathe and nourish the tissues.

Red Corpuscles or Erythrocytes (Fig. 1) are non-nucleated bi-concave discs, $\frac{1}{3200}$" in diameter. They contain *haemoglobin*, which can absorb oxygen to become *oxyhaemoglobin*, bright red in colour, then lose oxygen to the tissues to become *reduced haemoglobin*, which has a bluish colour. Red blood cells are produced in red bone marrow. They are partially disintegrated in the spleen, the process being completed in the liver. The normal red cell count is 5,000,000 per c.mm. of blood in the male, 4,500,000 in the female. These cells are the oxygen carriers of the blood.

White Corpuscles are larger, nucleated cells of 2 main types:
  (*a*) *Lymphocytes*, produced in lymph nodes and in the spleen.
  (*b*) *Leucocytes*, produced in the bone marrow. These leucocytes are of several types:
      polymorphonuclear neutrophil cells, forming 60–70 % of the total white cells; *eosinophil cells*, 1–4 %; *basophil cells*, 1 %; *monocytes*, 1–2 %; *transitional cells*, 2–8 %.

The normal white cell count is 6,000 to 10,000 per c.mm.; i.e. 1 white to 500 red cells. The white cells (*a*) protect the body against infection by their power of ingesting bacteria (*phagocytosis*); (*b*) help to disintegrate and liquefy tissue debris.

Platelets or Thrombocytes, average 250,000 per c.mm. of blood. They are essential for blood coagulation because of the enzyme *thrombokinase* which they contain. They are derived from large multinucleated cells (*megakaryocytes*) in the bone marrow.

THE LYMPHATIC SYSTEM
(Fig. 15)

Lymph is plasma after it has exuded from the capillaries. It gives nourishment to the tissue cells and receives their waste products. It is drained off by tiny lymphatic vessels which join to form larger lymph vessels.

Lymph vessels all convey lymph towards the heart. Their walls are plentifully supplied with valves.

Along the course of the lymph vessels are tiny masses of lymphoid tissue, the *lymph nodes* or *glands*. They vary in size from a pin head to a pea. All are invested in capsules. They:

(a) filter lymph as it passes through, and in this way often prevent infection from passing into the blood stream;

(b) add lymphocytes to the lymph.

The principal groups of lymph nodes are:

Occipital nodes, which drain the back of the scalp.

Retro-auricular nodes, which drain the area round the ear.

Sub-mental and *sub-mandibular nodes*, which drain the face and floor of the mouth.

Superficial cervical nodes, which drain the external ear and neck.

Deep cervical nodes, which drain the tongue, lower pharynx, larynx and thyroid.

Axillary nodes, which drain the upper limbs and breasts.

Supra- or *epitrochlear* or *cubital nodes*, which drain the hands and forearms.

Sternal nodes, which drain the front of the chest and the abdominal wall.

Intercostal nodes, which drain the chest wall.

Mediastinal nodes, which drain the heart, pericardium and thymus.

Bronchial nodes, which drain the lungs.

Coeliac nodes, which drain the stomach, spleen, pancreas and liver.

Mesenteric nodes, which drain the intestines.

Lumbar nodes, which drain the kidneys, adrenals, ovaries and testes.

Internal iliac nodes, which drain the pelvic viscera.

External iliac nodes, which drain the groins.

Superficial inguinal nodes, which drain the buttocks, anus, perineum, the external genitals, and nearly all the superficial lymph of the lower limbs.

Deep inguinal nodes, which drain the deep tissues of the lower limbs.

Popliteal nodes, which drain the legs.

All lymph is eventually passed into 2 lymph vessels:

(a) the thoracic duct and (b) the R. lymphatic duct.

The *thoracic duct* arises as the *cisterna chyli* at the level of the 2nd lumber vertebra, and passes up through the abdomen and chest for 15 to 18 inches, to open into the blood stream at the junction of the left internal jugular and the left subclavian veins. The thoracic duct drains both lower limbs, pelvis, abdomen, left side of the head, neck, chest and left arm.

The *right lymphatic duct*, which is ½" long, drains the right side of the head, neck, chest and right arm, opening into the blood stream at the junction of the right internal jugular and the right subclavian veins.

The Spleen (Figs. 19 and 20): a purple organ, 5" long × 3" broad, weighing 7 ozs., lies in the L. hypochondrium behind the stomach, under cover of the 9th, 10th and 11th left ribs. It is convex laterally and concave medially, where vessels enter and leave (the *hilum*). It is surrounded by the fibro-muscular *splenic capsule*, which sends septa, the *trabeculae*, into the organ to support the splenic pulp.

The splenic artery (from the coeliac artery) enters the spleen and breaks up into smaller vessels which terminate abruptly, allowing the blood to escape into the splenic pulp. The *splenic vein* drains the spleen.

The functions of the spleen are not clearly understood, and it is not a vital organ.

(*a*) It helps to produce the white corpuscles, *lymphocytes*.

(*b*) It initiates the disintegration of red corpuscles, a process completed in the liver.

(*c*) It acts as a store-house for blood; e.g. in haemorrhage and severe muscular exercise it expels blood into the circulation.

THE NERVOUS SYSTEM

A *nerve cell* or *neurone* (Fig. 1) consists of a *nerve cell body* with its receiving processes the *dendrites*, its transmitting process the *axon* and its *nerve endings*.

Medullated or *white nerve fibres* are processes of the cell body covered with *myelin* and enclosed in the *sheath of Schwann* or *neurolemma*. *Non-medullated* or *grey nerve fibres* have no myelin. The *grey matter* of the brain and spinal cord consists of masses of nerve cells, the *white matter* of medullated fibres.

Motor or *efferent nerves* control the movement of muscles and the secretion of glands.

Sensory or *afferent nerves* carry impulses from the sensory nerve endings to cells in the C.N.S.

Mixed nerves consist of motor and sensory fibres.

A *nerve ganglion* is a mass of nerve cells lying outside the brain or cord.

A *nerve centre* is a mass of cells, lying within the brain or cord, controlling one particular function; e.g. speech centre.

A *nerve plexus* is a network of fibres.

A *synapse* is the point where one neurone transmits its impulse to another neurone; the axon of one touches the cell body or dendrite of another but there is no continuity of cell substance from one neurone to the other.

The Central Nervous System (C.N.S.), Fig. 16, includes the brain and the spinal cord.

The Brain is covered externally by 3 membranes, *the meninges*: the *dura mater*, the outer layer; the *arachnoid*, the middle layer; the *pia mater*, the inner layer, adherent to the brain. *Cerebro-spinal fluid* (C.S.F.), resembling lymph, surrounds the brain in the *subarachnoid* space (between the arachnoid and pia mater), and fills the *ventricles* within the brain. The four principal ventricles are:

> R. and L. *lateral ventricles*, one in each cerebral hemisphere. They communicate with the *third ventricle* by the *interventricular foramina (of Munro)*, and it, in turn, with the *fourth ventricle* lying in the medulla, by the *cerebral aqueduct (of Sylvius)*. The 4th ventricle communicates with the *central canal* of the spinal cord.

The 4 principal parts of the brain are:

Cerebrum (Fig. 16).

Grey matter (i.e. nerve cells) form the outer layer or *cortex*, arranged in *convolutions*. White matter (i.e. nerve fibres) underlies the cortex. The *longitudinal fissure*, containing a fold of dura mater, the *falx cerebri*, separates the R. and L. *cerebral hemispheres*, which are further divided into *lobes* named after the overlying skull bones: the *frontal, parietal, occipital, temporal* lobes, and also the *insula* or *island of Reil*. All these lobes contain important *centres*. The *corpus callosum* joins the two cerebral hemispheres in the depths of the longitudinal fissure. *Basal ganglia* are small masses of grey matter within the white matter of the cerebral hemispheres. The most important:

> (1) The *thalami*, one on each side, are concerned chiefly with transmitting sensory impulses from the cord and medulla to the cerebral cortex.
>
> (2) The *corpora striata* are striped because of intermingling of white and grey matter. They transmit motor impulses from the cortex to other parts of the brain and cord.

The *internal capsule* is the white matter between the basal ganglia. Its fibres connect centres in the cortex with those in the brain stem and spinal cord.

Choroid plexuses, fringed, vascular processes, projecting into the ventricles, produce the cerebrospinal fluid.

Function of the cerebrum:

> (a) Controls all voluntary movement. (The great motor area lies in front of the *central sulcus* (fissure of Rolando), between the frontal and parietal lobes.)
>
> (b) Interprets all conscious sensation. (The great sensory area lies behind the central sulcus.)
>
> (c) Is the seat of all higher functions, such as memory, speech, emotions, etc.

The Cerebellum (Fig. 16) lies below and behind the cerebrum. It has grey

matter overlying white matter, and its R. and L. hemispheres are partially divided by a fold of dura mater, the *falx cerebelli*. It controls muscular co-ordination and balance.

The Pons (Fig. 16) ($1\frac{1}{2}''$ long × 2″ wide) is a bridge of nerve fibres linking

the R. and L. cerebellar hemispheres, and also linking the cerebellum with the cerebrum above and the medulla below. All impulses passing between the brain and the cord traverse the pons.

The Medulla Oblongata ($1\frac{1}{4}''$ long, greatest width $\frac{3}{4}''$) is continuous with

the pons above and the cord below. It consists of intermingled white and grey matter. The white matter (i.e. nerve fibres) forms *tracts*. *The pyramidal tracts* anteriorly convey motor impulses downwards from the brain. Most of these motor fibres cross at the *decussation of pyramids*, thus the motor area of one side of the brain controls the opposite side of the body.

Posteriorly are the sensory fibres which convey sensory impulses upwards from the cord to the brain. These fibres cross at different levels.

In the lateral part of the medulla are bundles of both motor and sensory fibres. The medulla contains many vital centres controlling temperature, respiration, etc.

The Cranial Nerves are 12 pairs given off from the base of the brain.

1. The *olfactory nerve* (sensory, of smell) passes from endings in the nasal mucosa, through the cribriform plate to enter the olfactory bulb, thence via the olfactory tract to the olfactory centre in the temporal lobe.

2. The *optic* nerve (sensory, of sight) passes, from endings in the retina, through the optic foramen. R. and L. nerves join to form the *optic chiasma*. Half the fibres in each nerve cross to the opposite side and all the fibres, crossed and uncrossed, send their impulses to the visual centre in the occipital lobe.

3. The *oculo-motor* nerve (motor) supplies the superior, inferior and medial rectus muscles, the levator palpebrae superioris, the sphincter of the iris, and the ciliary muscles.

4. The *trochlear* nerve (motor) supplies the superior oblique muscle of the eye.

5. The *trigeminal* nerve (mixed); motor fibres pass to the muscles of mastication, secretory fibres pass to sweat and lacrimal glands. The sensory fibres are the principal sensory nerves of the face. The sensory root is expanded to form the *semilunar (Gasserian) ganglion*, situated over the apex of the petrous part of the temporal bone. From this ganglion three large sensory nerves pass out:

(i) The *ophthalmic* nerve passes along the outer wall of the cavernous sinus and enters the orbit through the superior orbital fissure. It divides to give off the lacrimal, frontal and nasociliary nerves. The *lacrimal nerve* pierces the palpebral fascia and supplies the skin of the upper eyelid. The *frontal* nerve divides into (a) the *supraorbital* nerve passing through the *supraorbital notch* and (b) the *supratrochlear* nerve medial to it, both distributed to forehead and scalp. The *nasociliary* nerve has two terminal branches: (a) the internal branch supplying the nasal septum, and (b) the external branch supplying the skin of the alae nasi and tip of the nose.

(ii) The *maxillary* nerve crosses the pterygopalatine fossa and passes out through the *infra-orbital foramen* (Fig. 2) to become the *infra-orbital* nerve, which gives off nasal, palpebral and labial nerves. These join with branches of the facial nerve.

(iii) The *mandibular* nerve passes out of the skull through the *foramen ovale*. Its branches include the auriculotemporal, buccal, inferior alveolar and the lingual which is joined by the chorda tympani.

6. The *abducent* nerve (motor), enters the orbit through the superior orbital fissure, to supply the lateral rectus muscle of the eye.

7. The *facial* nerve (mixed) enters the internal acoustic (auditory) meatus with the 8th nerve (Fig. 24) and runs a tortuous course through the temporal bone giving off the *chorda tympani* which contains taste fibres for the anterior $\frac{2}{3}$ of the tongue and secretory fibres for the submandibular and sublingual glands.

The facial nerve emerges from the skull by the stylo-mastoid foramen and passes into the parotid gland where it divides to supply the muscles of the face.

8. The *auditory (stato-acoustic)* nerve (sensory) passes into the ear through the internal acoustic meatus and divides into:

(*a*) The *cochlear* nerve, to the cochlea, the organ of hearing.

(*b*) The *vestibular* nerve to the semi-circular canals, utricle and saccule, the organs of balance.

9. The *glosso-pharyngeal* nerve (mixed) leaves the cranium through the jugular foramen. It gives off pharyngeal branches (sensory) to the pharyngeal mucosa, tonsillar branches (sensory) to the tonsil, fauces and soft palate; lingual branches (sensory, of taste) to the posterior $\frac{1}{3}$ of the tongue.

10. The *vagus* nerve (mixed) passes out through the jugular foramen, down the side of the neck, giving off meningeal, auricular, pharyngeal, superior and recurrent laryngeal and cervical cardiac nerves. The vagus passes down through the chest, giving off thoracic cardiac, pulmonary and oesophageal nerves, thence through the diaphragm as the gastric nerves.

11. The *spinal accessory* nerve passes out through the jugular foramen to supply the sterno-mastoid and trapezius muscles.

12. The *hypoglossal* nerve (motor) supplies the tongue.

The Spinal Cord, $17''$ long $\times \frac{1}{2}''$ diameter, lies in the vertebral canal. It extends from the medulla to the level of the 2nd lumbar vertebra, where it branches into fibres, the *cauda equina*. It is surrounded by the same three meninges as the brain. C.S.F. surrounds it in the sub-arachnoid space, and is contained also in the *central canal*, traversing the centre of the cord. The cord is partially cleft by the deep *anterior median fissure* and the smaller *posterior median groove*. White nerve matter forms the outer substance of the cord; sensory nerve fibres posteriorly and motor nerve fibres anteriorly. Grey matter within the cord is arranged like a butterfly with outstretched wings. The wings terminate as *cornua* or *horns*. Posterior horns receive sensory fibres; anterior horns give off motor fibres. Corresponding motor and sensory fibres join up to form the *mixed spinal nerves* which emerge from between the vertebrae. Thirty-one pairs of spinal nerves are so formed:

8 pairs of cervical nerves
12   ,,   ,, thoracic   ,,
5   ,,   ,, lumbar   ,,
5   ,,   ,, sacral   ,,
1 pair ,, coccygeal ,,

On issuing from the vertebral canal, the spinal nerves again divide; the *ventral rami (divisions)* supply areas in front of the spinal column, the *dorsal rami (divisions)* supply skin and muscles behind it. In all regions except the thoracic, the ventral rami form plexuses:

Cervical plexus, formed by the first 4 cervical nerves, sends fibres to the anterior and lateral muscles of the neck. The *phrenic nerve*, its largest branch, passes from 3rd, 4th and 5th cervical segments, down through the chest to supply the diaphragm.

The *brachial plexus*, formed by lower 4 cervical and 1st thoracic nerves, sends branches to the shoulder and upper limb. Larger branches to the shoulder girdle include the long thoracic nerve (of Bell), supra-scapular, and pectoral nerves. To the arm, the *radial* nerve winds round the humerus from back to front, and below the elbow-joint gives off the *posterior interosseous* nerve. The *ulnar nerve* supplies the inner border of the arm. The *median nerve* runs down the front of the arm and forearm.

The *thoracic nerves*. Dorsal rami supply the muscles and skin of the back. Ventral rami form the *intercostal nerves* passing to the *intercostal* and abdominal muscles and overlying skin.

The *lumbar plexus* is formed by the ventral rami of 1st 4 lumbar nerves. It supplies the groin and the front and side of the thigh. Its branches include the *ilio-hypogastric, ilio-inguinal, obturator,* and *femoral nerves,* which give off branches to anterior and medial thigh muscles. The *saphenous* nerve arises from the femoral nerve, and passes down the medial border of the leg to the foot.

The *sacral plexus* is formed by the ventral rami of the 4th and 5th lumbar nerves, the first 3 and part of the 4th sacral nerves. Its branches include:

> *sup.* and *inf. gluteal nerves* to the gluteal muscles; the *pudendal* nerve to the rectum, perineum, and ext. genitals; the *posterior cutaneous nerve of thigh* to the back of the thigh and ext. genitals; the *sciatic* nerve passes deeply through the gluteal and thigh muscles. About the middle of the thigh it branches to form the *tibial nerve,* and the *common peroneal nerve.*

The remaining sacral and coccygeal nerves supply the skin and muscles overlying the coccyx and also send fibres to the pelvic viscera.

The Autonomic Nervous System supplies all the structures over which we have no voluntary control, such as the viscera, vessels, and glands. It can be divided into 2 distinct parts:

1. The sympathetic system.
2. The parasympathetic system.

The Sympathetic System consists of a gangliated cord on either side and in front of the vertebral column, extending downwards from the neck to join its neighbour of the opposite side in a loop in front of the coccyx.

Small fibres, *the white rami communicantes,* run to these sympathetic ganglia from the ventral rami of the corresponding spinal nerves. Larger fibres, *the grey rami,* pass from the ganglia throughout the body to supply all plain muscle and glands.

The principal sympathetic plexuses are:

> The *deep* and *superficial cardiac plexuses* which supply all the thoracic viscera and accompany the thoracic vessels.
>
> The *solar* or *coeliac plexus* surrounds the coeliac axis. Branches supply all the abdominal viscera and form secondary plexuses in connection with the great vessels; e.g. the phrenic plexus accompanies the phrenic artery, the renal plexus accompanies the renal artery, etc.
>
> The *superior hypogastric plexus* lies between the R. and L. common iliac arteries. It divides to form 2 *inferior hypogastric (pelvic) plexuses,* which form secondary plexuses to supply the pelvic viscera and vessels; e.g. the haemorrhoidal plexus to the rectum, the vesical plexus to the bladder, the uterine plexus to the uterus, etc.

The influence of the supra-renal secretion in stimulating the sympathetic system is mentioned on page 56.

The Parasympathetic System consists of fibres which arise from certain cranial and sacral nerves.

(*a*) Fibres which arise in the mid brain to join the 3rd cranial nerve, supplying the ciliary muscle and the sphincter of the iris.

(*b*) Fibres arising in the medulla, to join the 7th, 9th and 11th cranial nerves.

(*c*) 10th cranial nerve.

(*d*) Fibres from the sacral nerves, which constitute the *pelvic splanchnic nerves*.

Every organ over which there is no voluntary control is supplied with fibres from the sympathetic and parasympathetic systems. These different fibres have opposing functions.

The *sympathetic fibres* increase the heart rate, raise the blood pressure and mobilise glucose, all of which combat fatigue; dilate the pupils and the bronchi; stimulate the secretion of sweat.

The *parasympathetic fibres* slow the heart, lower the blood pressure, contract the pupils, constrict the bronchi, and decrease the secretion of sweat.

It has been said that the sympathetic system provides for the work of to-day, and that its action is increased during physical activity; while the parasympathetic system provides for to-morrow as it is mainly concerned with changes taking place during rest.

MEMBRANES

Membranes are of several types.

1. **Mucous Membrane** lines every tract communicating with the exterior, either directly or indirectly. Its mucous glands secrete *mucin* or *mucus*. Mucous membrane lines:

(*a*) The alimentary tract, i.e. from the mouth to the rectum.

(*b*) The respiratory tract, i.e. from the nose to the lungs.

(*c*) The urinary tract, i.e. from the urethra to pelves of the kidneys.

(*d*) The genital tract, i.e. from the vulva to the fallopian tubes of the female, and from the urethra to the epididymes of the male.

2. **Serous Membrane** has, with one exception (the female peritoneum), no communication with the exterior. It covers internal organs and lines the cavities containing them. Each serous membrane has 2 layers; the inner or *visceral* layer, which is closely adherent to the organ, and the outer or *parietal* layer, which lines the cavity. These layers form a closed sac containing a small quantity of serous fluid.

(i) **The Pleura** (Figs. 18, 19) covers the lungs (page 54).

(ii) **The Pericardium** (Figs. 18, 19) covers the heart (page 37).

(iii) **The Peritoneum** covers the abdominal organs and lines the abdominal cavity. Different parts have different names, but it consists of one continuous sheet.

(a) *The omentum* is that part of the peritoneum attached to the stomach. The *lesser omentum* (Fig. 19) passes from the upper border of the stomach to the porta hepatis. The *greater omentum* (Fig. 18) is attached to the lower border of the stomach, hanging down apron-like in front of the intestines. The *gastro-splenic ligament* passes between the stomach and the spleen.

(b) *The mesentery* (Fig. 19) is that part of the peritoneum attached to the intestines. The greater part anchors the small intestine to the posterior abdominal wall. It contains the superior mesenteric vessels and numerous lymph nodes. The *meso-colon* anchors the colon to the posterior wall of the abdomen and the brim of the pelvis.

(c) The *recto-uterine pouch* (*of Douglas*) is a pouch of peritoneum dipping down into the female pelvis between the uterus and rectum. It contains coils of intestine.

(d) The *recto-vesical pouch* is a similar pouch in the male pelvis between the bladder and rectum.

3. **Synovial Membrane.** See page 36 (Joints).

THE DIGESTIVE SYSTEM

The Digestive System changes complex food into simple substances which can be absorbed. It includes:

1. **The Alimentary Tract,** extending from the mouth to the rectum.

2. Certain **Digestive Glands** (3 pairs of salivary glands, the liver and the pancreas) not in the alimentary tract, but which pass their secretions into it. These secretions are necessary for digestion.

The Alimentary Tract includes: the mouth, pharynx, oesophagus, stomach, small and large intestines.

The Mouth. Its boundaries are: 2 maxillary bones above; 1 mandible below; 2 palatine bones forming part of the roof. Cheek muscles are lateral, the lips anterior, mylo-hyoid muscles form the floor and the soft palate lies postero-superiorly. The soft palate is prolonged backwards and downwards from the hard palate and forms a partial partition between the mouth and the pharynx. (In swallowing, the soft palate directs food downwards and prevents it regurgitating through the nose.)

The pillars of the fauces or *palatine arches* form the sides of the aperture between the mouth and the pharynx. There is an anterior and posterior pillar at each side. Between these pillars lie the *palatine tonsils*.

The mouth contains *teeth* embedded in the *alveolar parts* of the jaws. Each tooth is composed of *dentine*. The *crown* projects from the gum; the *root* or *fang* is embedded in the gum; the *neck* is between the crown and the root. *Enamel* covers the crown; *cement* covers the root. The *pulp cavity* contains the blood vessels and nerves.

The *permanent teeth* are 32 in number. On each side, in each jaw, there are, from before backwards—2 *incisors*, 1 *canine* (eye tooth), 2 *premolars* or *bicuspids* and 3 *molars*.

The *milk* or *deciduous teeth* number 10 in each jaw—2 *incisors*, 1 *canine* and 2 *molars* on each side.

D

The Tongue, consisting of striated voluntary muscle, is attached mainly to the mandible and hyoid bone. Its covering of mucous membrane is smooth inferiorly, raised to form a ridge or *frenulum* below the tip and roughened superiorly by *papillae. Fungiform papillae* lie at the tip and sides of the tongue. *Filiform papillae* are distributed over the surface. *Vallate papillae,* the largest, lie in a V formation posteriorly; at the bases of these papillae lie the *taste buds.*

Blood vessels: *lingual arteries* from the ext. carotid arteries.

Nerves: of taste, branches of 7th and 9th cranial; of other sensations, branches of 5th cranial; motor nerves, 12th cranial.

The Pharynx is a wide muscular tube, $4\frac{1}{2}''$ to $5''$ long, lined with stratified squamous epithelium and extending from the base of the skull to the level of the 6th cervical vertebra.

The *naso-pharynx* is that part lying above and behind the mouth. The pharynx has seven openings:

> 2 *posterior apertures of the nose* into the naso-pharynx.
> 2 *auditory (Eustachian) tubes* pass from the ears to the naso-pharynx.
> 1 opening from the mouth.
> 1 opening into the larynx from the distal end of the pharynx anteriorly.
> 1 opening into the oesophagus from the distal end posteriorly.

The three constrictor muscles of the pharynx account for the thickness of its wall and play a large part in swallowing.

Nerves of the pharynx: 9th and 10th cranial.

Blood vessels: ascending pharyngeal, palatine and tonsillar arteries.

The Oesophagus (Fig. 18) is a muscular tube, $9''$–$10''$ long, which passes downwards from the distal end of the pharynx. It passes through the neck behind the trachea, through the chest, pierces the diaphragm, and enters the stomach. From the oesophagus onwards, the wall of the alimentary tract has much the same basic structure:

> (i) Lining mucous membrane.
> (ii) Submucous layer of connective tissue.
> (iii) Circular muscle fibres.
> (iv) Longitudinal muscle fibres.

Nerves are from the 10th cranial.

Blood vessels are the oesophageal arteries.

The Stomach (Figs. 18 and 19) is a muscular sac lying in the L. hypochondrium and epigastrium. Its size and shape vary with its contents and muscle tone. The structure of its wall is like that of the oesophagus with the addition of an extra layer of oblique muscle fibres and covering of peritoneum.

The oesophagus opens into the *cardiac end;* the duodenum passes out from the *pyloric end.* The *greater curvature* is the left border, the *lesser curvature* the right border. *Gastric glands* are tubular glands secreting an enzyme *pepsin.* The *oxyntic* or *parietal cells* in these glands secrete HCl. The stomach mucous membrane secretes the intrinsic blood-building factor of Castle which is stored in the liver.

Blood vessels: gastric, pyloric, and gastro-epiploic arteries.

Nerves: from vagi and coeliac plexus (sympathetic system).

Small Intestine (Fig. 18) is a muscular tube 20′–22′ long, its coils occupying the greater part of the abdominal cavity. It consists of the *duodenum* (Figs. 19,

20), 8″–10″ long; the *jejunum*, 8′, and the *ileum* 12′. The lining mucous membrane forms permanent circular folds which (*a*) provide a larger surface for digestion and absorption; (*b*) delay progress of the intestinal contents. These folds are absent from the first inch of the duodenum and the last part of the ileum. *Villi* are tiny projections of the lining, giving it a bath-towel appearance. Each villus contains a *lacteal* for absorption of fat and a capillary loop for absorption of protein and sugar.

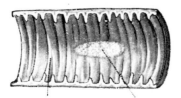

| Circular folds (valvulae conniventes) | Aggregated lymphatic nodules (Peyer's patch) |

THE INTERIOR OF A PORTION OF THE ILEUM

Glands of the small intestine: mucous glands secrete mucin; *duodena (Brunner's) glands* are racemose glands lying in the submucosa of the duodenum; *intestinal glands* or *crypts of Lieberkühn* are tubular glands opening between the villi. The combined secretion of these intestinal glands is intestinal juice or *succus entericus*. It contains enzymes for the digestion of protein and sugars.

In the lining of the small intestine, especially in the ileum, there are patches of lymphoid tissue, the *solitary lymphatic follicles*; *Peyer's patches* or *aggregated lymphatic follicles* are merely large collections of solitary follicles.

Blood vessels: superior mesenteric artery.

Nerves: branches from the solarplexus.

The Large Intestine (Fig. 19) wider than the small intestine, but shorter, is 5′ to 6′ long. It forms three sides of a rectangle surrounding the coils of small intestine. Different parts of the large intestine:

(i) The *caecum*, into which the ileum opens. This orifice is guarded by the *ileo-caecal valve*, allowing an onflow and preventing a backflow of intestinal contents. The caecum is a dilated pouch 2½″ long × 3″ wide, lying in the right iliac fossa.

(ii) *The vermiform appendix*, averaging 3″ long, is attached to the caecum and terminates in a blind end.

(iii) The *ascending colon* passes up the right side of the abdomen, to bend sharply under the liver at

(iv) *The right (hepatic) flexure*. From here

(v) *The transverse colon* passes across the abdomen from right to left, and in the left hypochondrium bends at

(vi) *The left (splenic) flexure*.

(vii) *The descending colon* passes down the left side of the abdomen to the iliac crest, where it takes a double **S**-shaped bend

(viii) *The sigmoid colon*, from which

(ix) *The rectum* passes down through the pelvis posteriorly. It is 5″ to 6″ long.

The last $1\frac{1}{2}''$ of rectum is the *anal canal* which terminates as the *anal orifice*. The mucosa of the large intestine has no circular folds, no villi, and its only glands are mucous glands. Most of the longitudinal muscle fibres are arranged in three bands, which are shorter than the other coats, and cause sacculation. Peritoneum does not cover the ascending or the descending colon posteriorly, nor the lower $\frac{1}{3}$ of the rectum.

3 Pairs of Salivary Glands

R. and *L. parotid glands* each lie in the crevice between the mandible and the ear and overflow on to the side of the mandible. From them run the *parotid* (*Stenson's*) *ducts* (2″ long), opening into the mouth at the level of the 2nd upper molar teeth.

R. and *L. submandibular glands* lie under cover of the body of the mandible. *Submandibular* (*Wharton's*) *ducts* open into the mouth under the tongue on either side of the frenulum.

R. and L. sublingual glands lie under the mucosa of the floor of the mouth. The *sublingual ducts* (*of Rivini*) (18–20 of them) open on to the floor of the mouth.

Their combined secretion is *saliva*, a clear watery alkaline fluid, S.G. 1003. It consists of water, salts, mucin, and the enzyme, *ptyalin* or *diastase*, which converts starch into sugar. About 2 pints are secreted per day.

The Liver (Figs. 18, 19) is the largest gland. It occupies the greater part of the R. hypochondrium; part of it lies in the epigastrium and L. hypochondrium. It measures about 10″–12″ across, 6″–7″ back to front, and weighs about 50 ozs. The *fissure* for the *ligamentum teres* on the inferior surface and the *fissure* for the *ligamentum venosum* on the posterior surface divide the liver into a large *right lobe* and a small *left lobe*. The right lobe includes the smaller *quadrate* and *caudate* lobes. Vessels enter and leave the liver by the *porta hepatis*, a fissure on the inferior surface of the right lobe. Between the liver and the diaphragm, the 2 layers of peritoneum which constitute the *falciform ligament* separate, as they are traced upwards, to form the *coronary ligament* and leave an area on the upper surface of the liver without a covering of peritoneum. The right and left *triangular ligaments* are the lateral edges of this coronary ligament. In the free edge of the falciform ligament below the edge of the liver runs the *ligamentum teres* (*round ligament*) which is the remains of the umbilical vein of the foetus.

Liver tissue consists of hexagonal *lobules*, each with a *central vein*; *interlobular* blood vessels run between the lobules.

The *hepatic artery* from the coeliac artery and the *portal vein* draining the digestive organs and spleen, both enter the liver at the *porta hepatis*, and their branches, surrounded by connective tissue, *Glisson's capsule*, run between the lobules. *Hepatic veins* drain venous blood from the liver, and open into the inferior vena cava.

Bile Ducts (Fig. 19). *R. and L. hepatic ducts* drain the R. and L. lobes of the liver, joining to form the *common hepatic duct* (2″ long). From the common hepatic duct, bile passes along the *cystic duct* ($1\frac{1}{2}''$) into the gall bladder, where it is stored and concentrated. When required, bile passes out of the gall bladder, via the cystic duct, into the *common bile duct* (3″ long). The common bile duct opens into the duodenum with the pancreatic duct through the *ampulla* (*of Vater*), about 4″ beyond the pylorus.

The Gall Bladder (Fig. 19) is a muscular, pear-shaped sac, lined with specialised mucous membrane, partially covered with peritoneum and attached to the under surface of the R. lobe of the liver. It is about 3″ long, and normally holds 1¼ ozs. It stores bile and concentrates it 8–10 times.

The Pancreas (Fig. 20) is a cream-coloured gland, 6″ to 8″ long and 1½″ wide. The *tail* lies against the spleen in the L. hypochondrium, the *body* passes in front of the L. kidney, behind the stomach, the *head* lies in the loop of the duodenum.

The gland consists of lobules from which ducts, conveying pancreatic juice, open into the *pancreatic duct*. The pancreatic duct passes out of the pancreas and opens into the duodenum, together with the common bile duct through the ampulla (of Vater).

The *islets of Langerhans*, specialised cells of the pancreas, secrete *insulin*, which is passed into the general circulation and controls sugar metabolism.

Blood vessels:

> the pancreatic arteries from the splenic artery,
> the superior pancreatico-duodenal artery from the hepatic artery, and
> the inferior pancreatico-duodenal artery from the superior mesenteric artery.

Nerves: from the coeliac plexus.

THE RESPIRATORY SYSTEM

The Respiratory System is the system by which blood is oxygenated and CO_2 and some water excreted. It includes the nose, pharynx, larynx, trachea, bronchi, bronchioles and lungs.

Nose. 2 *nasal* bones form the bridge; the *vomer*, the *perpendicular plate* of the *ethmoid* and the *septal cartilage* form the mid-line *nasal septum*; each lateral wall consists of the *maxilla* (which includes the *superior* and *middle conchae*), the *inferior concha* and the *vertical plate* of the *palatine bone*; the *palatine processes* of the maxillae and the *horizontal plates* of the palatine bones lie in the floor while the *cribriform plate* of the *ethmoid* and the body of the *sphenoid* are in the roof; the pliable tissue around the nostrils consists of cartilage and muscle. The lining mucous membrane is highly vascular and continuous with that of the nasopharynx through the *posterior apertures* of the nose.

Under each of the three conchae (superior, middle and inferior) lies the corresponding meatus; into the *superior meatus* open the sphenoidal and posterior ethmoidal air sinuses, into the *middle meatus* the frontal, maxillary and anterior ethmoidal and into the *inferior* the nasolacrimal duct.

The nose (*a*) warms, filters and moistens inspired air; (*b*) is the special sense organ of smell; (*c*) aids phonation.

The Pharynx forms part of the respiratory and alimentary tracts. It is the only part of the respiratory tract not lined with ciliated epithelium. (See page 50).

The Larynx or voice box is formed of cartilages joined by ligaments and muscles.

The thyroid cartilage (Figs. 18, 19), the Adam's apple, consists of two plates joined at an acute angle anteriorly and open posteriorly.

The *cricoid cartilage* (Fig. 18), immediately below the thyroid cartilage, is exactly like a signet ring, narrow anteriorly and wider posteriorly.

The *arytenoid cartilages* (2) are pyramidal in shape and sit, side by side, on the upper edge of the cricoid posteriorly.

The *vestibular folds* (false vocal cords) are two folds of mucous membrane covering strands of skeletal muscle stretching across the larynx from the inside of the angle of the thyroid cartilage to the front of the arytenoid cartilages; the *vocal folds* (true vocal cords), immediately below the vestibular folds, each run from inside the angle of the thyroid cartilage to the pointed *vocal process* of the arytenoid cartilage. The tension of the vocal folds and hence the pitch of the voice depend on the activity of the muscle fibres underlying the mucous membrane.

The *glottis* is the space between the vocal folds; its size varies with the movement of the vocal processes of the arytenoids to and from the midline, decreasing or increasing it respectively.

The *epiglottis* is a leaf-shaped cartilage attached to the posterior wall of the thyroid cartilage. It guards the superior aperture of the larynx.

Blood vessels are the laryngeal arteries. Nerves are the superior and recurrent laryngeal nerves.

The Trachea or windpipe (Figs. 18, 19, 20) measures $4\frac{1}{2}''$ long $\times$ 1" wide. It extends from the level of the 6th cervical vertebra to the 4th thoracic vertebra, passing through the neck in front of the oesophagus. It consists of 16–20 horseshoe shaped bars of cartilage united by fibrous tissue and unstriped muscle. Anteriorly the trachea is rigid, posteriorly its walls are soft and yielding. The trachea bifurcates to form:

The Bronchi (Fig. 20). The R. bronchus is 1" long, the L. bronchus is 2". As with the trachea, the walls of the bronchi are strengthened by the presence of small irregular plates of cartilage. The bronchi branch into smaller and smaller tubes and finally into the *bronchioles*; these have no cartilage in their walls and end as *alveolar ducts* from which there spring clusters of thin-walled *air sacs* or *alveoli*. Between the alveoli run the pulmonary capillaries; oxygen passes from the air in the alveoli into the blood in the capillaries and carbon dioxide from the capillaries to the alveoli.

The Lungs (Fig. 18) are two greyish-pink and spongy, cone-shaped bodies occupying the greater part of the chest. The apices pass upwards behind the clavicles; the bases rest on the diaphragm. On the medial surface of each lung is *the root*, where blood vessels and the bronchus enter. The R. lung has three lobes, upper, middle, and lower. The L. lung has two lobes, an upper and lower.

Serous membrane, the *pleura* (Figs. 18, 19, 20) covers the lungs. The visceral layer closely invests the lung tissue; the parietal layer lines the chest wall. Between these layers is the *pleural cavity*, a potential space. *Diaphragmatic pleura* covers the superior surface of the diaphragm; *costal pleura* adheres to the ribs.

Blood vessels: 3 bronchial arteries, 2 to the L. lung and one to the R. lung.

Nerves: 10th cranial and sympathetic branches from the pulmonary plexuses.

THE URINARY SYSTEM

The Urinary System includes the kidneys, ureters, bladder and urethra.

The Kidneys (Figs. 20, 21) are 2 bean-shaped organs, 4″ long × 2″ wide × 1″ thick lying against the posterior abdominal wall at the normal waist line, the right being slightly lower than the left. Each kidney is surrounded by a fibrous capsule, and is maintained in position by:

    (*a*)   the perinephric fat;

    (*b*)   the peritoneum, which covers it anteriorly but not posteriorly;

    (*c*)   the vessels which enter and leave at the *hilum*. One renal artery enters, one renal vein and one ureter leave each kidney.

The *cortex* is the outer layer of light reddish-brown tissue.

The *medulla* is the middle dark brown portion.

The *pelvis* is the hollow, inner portion from which the ureter opens.

Kidney tissue is composed of structures called *nephrons*, supported by connective tissue. The nephrons consist of the uriniferous tubules and their associated blood vessels. The uriniferous tubules all originate in the cortex as *glomerular (Bowman's) capsules*, from which the *proximal convoluted tubules* pass out. The tubules then pass downwards into the medulla and back into the cortex to form the *loops of Henle*; again they twist in the cortex as the *distal convoluted tubules*, and again pass downwards to the medulla. Here the smaller uriniferous tubules form larger *collecting tubules*. Collecting tubules are massed together to form the *pyramids*, which open into the kidney pelvis through the *calyces*.

Afferent blood vessels (branches of the renal artery) pass into the glomerular capsules and form capillary loops, the *glomeruli*. These glomeruli and their surrounding capsules form *renal corpuscles (Malpighian bodies)*.

Efferent blood vessels pass out of the capsules to twine round and supply the tubules throughout their course.

The function of the kidney is to separate certain waste products from the blood, and it is very largely this renal function which maintains the blood at a constant composition, notwithstanding great variations in diet and fluid intake.

As the blood circulates in the glomeruli, a large quantity of water, salts, urea, and glucose are filtered into the capsules and thence into the convoluted tubules; here all the glucose, most of the water and salts, and some urea are returned to the blood vessels. The remainder passes into the collecting tubules and thence by the pyramids and calyces into the kidney pelvis as *urine*.

The Ureters (Fig. 20) are narrow muscular tubes, 10″–12″ long. They are lined with mucous membrane and lie behind the peritoneum. They pass down from the kidneys to open obliquely into the posterior wall of the bladder.

The Bladder (Figs. 18, 19, 20, 26) is a highly elastic muscular sac, normally lying in the true pelvis anteriorly, immediately behind the symphysis pubis. It is lined with mucous membrane, and covered posteriorly, but not anteriorly, by peritoneum. The *trigone* is the triangular portion of the bladder between the orifices of the ureters above and the urethra below.

The Urethra (Figs. 27 and 28) is a narrow muscular tube, lined with mucous membrane, passing from the bladder to open externally as the urinary meatus. The female urethra is 1″–1½″ long; the male urethra is 6″–8″ long.

THE ENDOCRINE SYSTEM

Endocrine or *ductless glands* or *glands of internal secretion* pass their secretions or *hormones* directly into the blood stream. The action of these hormones is therefore general, not local.

The Pituitary Gland or Hypophysis is a reddish structure, about the size of a pea, lying in the *hypophyseal* or *pituitary fossa* of the sphenoid bone. Its *anterior* (*pars distalis*) and *posterior* (*pars nervosa*) *lobes* are joined by the *pars intermedia*.

The *anterior lobe* secretes many hormones including the growth hormone controlling growth of the skeleton, gonadotrophic hormones for gonad activity both male and female, thyrotrophic and adrenocorticotrophic hormones regulating the thyroid and adrenal cortex respectively, and metabolic hormones. Because of its important part in the regulating the other ductless glands, the hypophysis has been called the leader of the endocrine orchestra.

The *posterior lobe* restricts the flow of urine by its anti-diuretic hormone, stimulates the uterus through its secretion of oxytocin and constricts the arterioles by vasopressin.

The Thyroid Gland (Figs. 18, 19) is situated just below the thyroid cartilage. R. and L. lobes lie one on each side of the trachea, united by the *isthmus*. Each lobe averages $1\frac{1}{2}''$ long $\times \frac{3}{4}''$ across, but the size varies physiologically as well as pathologically. The thyroid secretion, *thyroxin*, stimulates metabolism, and largely influences both mental and physical activity.

The 4 Parathyroid Glands lie, 2 on each side, behind the thyroid, partially embedded in thyroid tissue. Their secretion, *parathormone*, raises the blood calcium, and maintains the balance of calcium and phosphorus in the blood and in bone.

The Thymus Gland (Fig. 18) is essentially a gland of youth. It attains its maximum size of about $2\frac{1}{2}''$ long at puberty. It then extends down from the neck into the chest. After puberty, the thymus begins to atrophy, and only a remnant exists in the adult.

Its secretion is thought to delay the development of sex organs; i.e. as the thymus atrophies, sex organs develop.

The Supra-Renal Glands or Adrenals (Fig. 20) are yellow triangular bodies, one at the upper pole of each kidney.

The outer layer or *cortex* produces a number of hormones called corticosteroids which:

(*a*) Control the sodium and potassium balance in the body.
(*b*) Stimulate the storage of glucose in the liver and raise the blood sugar.
(*c*) Inhibit the formation of intercellular substances in connective tissues.
(*d*) Influence or supplement the production of sex hormones; tumours of the adrenal cortex are associated with hermaphroditism and virilism.

The inner layer or *medulla* produces adrenalin, which is a powerful vasoconstrictor. It raises the blood pressure by constriction of the smaller blood vessels and raises the blood sugar by promoting the output of sugar from the liver.

Physiologically (and anatomically) the medulla is closely associated with the sympathetic nervous system. Any factor (e.g. emotions such as fear) which stimulates the sympathetic system also stimulates the medulla and indirectly affects the cortex as well.

Other endocrine glands include:

The pancreas: see page 53.
The ovaries: see page 61.
The testes: see page 61.

SKIN

The Skin (Fig. 22) consists of two main layers, the epidermis or outer layer and the dermis or corium.

The *epidermis* is composed of stratified squamous epithelium (Fig. 1). It varies in thickness from $\frac{1}{240}''$ to $\frac{1}{24}''$, being thickest on soles and palms, thinnest on the flexor surfaces of the limbs. Free nerve endings are found in the epidermis but it has no blood vessels, being nourished by tissue fluid derived from the dermis. The dermis and epidermis are normally closely adherent and where they meet, there is a series of elevations, the *dermal papillae*; these are most numerous and regular in the finger tips, palms and soles and are responsible for the tiny *epidermal ridges* seen in those areas. The pattern of these ridges is constant and characteristic for each individual throughout life—the finger print, palm print and sole print—each of which can be a means of identification.

The *dermis* is a thicker layer of connective tissue, which supports various structures, such as:

Hairs. Each hair grows from a *hair follicle*, a minute pit passing obliquely down into the dermis. At the root, the hair is expanded to form the *hair bulb* into which a capillary loop passes.

The *arrector pili muscles* are attached to the hair follicles. These muscles contract in response to cold and fear, pull on the follicles and cause the skin to assume the typical 'goose skin' appearance.

Sebaceous glands secrete *sebum*, a fatty material which is passed into the hair follicles and thence on to the skin surface.

Sweat or sudoriferous glands are long tubular glands coiled at their bases, lying deeply embedded in the dermis. They extract water, salts, urea, and other waste products from the surrounding networks of capillaries and discharge these via ducts on to the skin surface as *sweat*. The secretion of sweat goes on constantly in health but evaporation keeps pace with secretion and we are unaware of it.

Different *sensory nerve endings* of the skin give sensations of touch, pain, pressure and temperature.

Superficial blood vessels, which pass up into the papillae, by their dilation and constriction, play a large part in regulating body temperature.

Adipose tissue, in the deeper layers of the dermis and in the subcutaneous tissues, forms a reserve food supply and helps to prevent undue loss of heat.

Nails are outgrowths from the epidermis and consist of flattened and horny epithelium. The root of the nail is the part covered by skin; the free edge projects beyond the tip of finger or toe; the body lies between the root and free edge. The lunula is the white half-moon area at the base of the nail. The martix is the bed of true skin on which the body of the nail lies and over which it grows.

The **Mammary Gland or Breast** (Fig. 23) is also a derivative of the epidermis. In the female it enlarges at puberty, and during pregnancy there is a further increase in size as it prepares to secrete milk (lactate) after the child is born. Each gland is hemispherical and extends under the skin of the chest wall from the level of the 2nd rib to the 6th rib and from the side of the sternum to the axilla. The secretory portion consists of 15–20 *lobules* each with a *lactiferous duct* converging and opening on the surface of the *nipple*. A great deal of fat encloses the lobules of each gland giving the breast its rounded appearance. Surrounding the nipple is a pigmented area of skin, the *areola*, containing small *areolar glands* to lubricate the nipple while the child is suckling. In the male the mammary gland remains rudimentary and is represented merely by a small nipple.

The blood vessels are branches of the internal thoracic, reaching the gland through the intercostal spaces, and of the lateral thoracic (Fig. 9).

The lymph drainage of the breast is important because cancer of the breast spreads by the lymph stream; it is chiefly to the lymph nodes in the axilla (Fig. 15).

THE EYE AND ITS APPENDAGES

Eyelids or *palpebrae* are muscular curtains covered with skin and lined with *conjunctiva*, a thin membrane covering the front of the eyeball and lining both lids. The *tarsi* or *tarsal plates* are tiny fibrous discs along the margins of the lids. *Tarsal (Meibomian) glands* open on the edge of the eyelids. The *lateral* or *outer commissure* or *canthus* is the outer angle between the lids; the *internal, medial* or *nasal commissure* or *canthus*, the inner angle. The *levator palpebrae superioris* (Fig. 25) is a thin flat muscle lying in the roof of the orbit. It is attached to the upper eyelid and is responsible for raising it. The eyeball is moved in the orbit by 6 muscles:

The *superior rectus* rotates the eyeball upwards and inwards.
The *inferior rectus* rotates downwards and inwards.
The *medial rectus* rotates the eyeball inwards.
The *lateral rectus* rotates the eyeball outwards.
The *superior oblique* rotates the eyeball downwards and outwards.
The *inferior oblique* rotates the eyeball upwards and outwards.

The *lacrimal* or *tear gland* lies in the *lacrimal fossa* of the frontal bone in the upper and outer part of the orbit. The watery secretion passes out via the *excretory ducts* opening on the inner surface of the upper eyelid where the conjunctiva is reflected off the eye on to the upper lid. It moistens and cleans the conjunctiva and normally drains away through the tiny *lacrimal puncta* (one punctum in the free edge of each lid near the inner canthus) into the *lacrimal canaliculi* and thence into the *lacrimal sac* and *nasolacrimal duct*. The nasolacrimal duct ($\frac{1}{2}''$ long) opens into the inferior meatus of the nose. Excess secretion of the lacrimal gland overflows on to the cheeks as tears.

The Eyeball (Fig. 25) is a hollow, spherical structure, contained in the orbit. Its wall consists of three main layers:

1. The *sclera* is the outer coat, tough, fibrous and opaque. It covers the posterior $\frac{5}{6}$ of the eyeball, becoming modified anteriorly to form the clear, transparent *cornea*, through which light enters the eyeball.

2. The *choroid* or middle coat, attached to the sclera, consists of an inter-lacement of blood vessels and pigment granules supported by loose connective tissue. Anteriorly the choroid becomes modified. Its outer layers terminate in the *iris*; inner layers in the *ciliary body*. The iris is a pigmented muscular curtain suspended behind the cornea from which it is separated by *aqueous humour*. In the centre of the iris is an aperture, the *pupil*, through which light reaches the interior of the eye.

The *circular* muscle fibres of the iris on contraction diminish the size of the pupil. The *radially* disposed fibres on contraction dilate the pupil. Thus the iris regulates the size of the pupil and the amount of light passing to the retina.

The *ciliary body* consists of *ciliary processes* and *ciliary muscles*. The former are 60 to 80 minute finger-like processes pointing towards the edge of the lens. The latter form a ring of plain muscle, underlying the ciliary processes. When these muscle fibres contract, they pull the ciliary processes forwards, relax the tension of the suspensory ligaments (see below), and with the decreased tension of its capsule, the lens becomes more convex or rounded. Conversely, on relaxa-tion of the ciliary muscles, the lens becomes less convex. Thus *accommodation* is obtained.

The *lens* is a transparent biconvex structure immediately behind and in con-tact with the edge of the iris. It is enclosed in a thin elastic capsule. From the periphery of the lens, *suspensory ligaments* pass out to be attached to the ciliary processes.

3. The *retina* forms the delicate inner layer of the eyeball, closely adherent to the choroid. It consists of 2 main strata; the outer chiefly of pigmented epi-thelium, the inner of nerve tissue, really an expansion of the optic nerve which enters the eyeball at the *optic disc*, or *blind spot*. In this layer are receptor or sensory optic nerve endings, the *rods and cones*.

The *anterior chamber* is the space between the cornea in front and the iris behind. The *posterior chamber* is a smaller space between the iris in front and the lens behind. Both chambers contain *aqueous humour*. The *vitreous body* or *humour* is a gelatinous substance occupying the greater part of the eyeball behind the lens. The *hyaloid membrane* encloses the vitreous body except in front, where it splits to enclose the lens.

THE EAR

(Fig. 24)

1. The *external ear* consists of (*a*) *the auricle* or *pinna*, and (*b*) the *external acoustic* or *auditory meatus* ($1\frac{1}{2}''$) which passes inwards from the pinna. Its floor curves upwards then downwards. In the lining skin are small hairs and *ceruminous glands* which secrete *cerumen* or wax.

The *drum* or *tympanic membrane* is a parchment-like membrane covered externally by stratified epithelium, internally by mucous membrane. It lies obliquely across the opening between the external and middle ears.

2. *Middle ear* or *tympanum* is a small cavity in the petrous portion of the temporal bone, $\frac{5}{8}''$ long $\times \frac{1}{2}''$ high $\times \frac{1}{2}''$ wide. It is bounded externally by the drum and internally by the internal ear. The *auditory ossicles*, 3 minute bones, stretch across the cavity: (*a*) the *malleus*, attached by its handle to the drum, (*b*) the *incus*, articulating with the malleus, and on the inner side with (*c*) the *stapes*. The base

of the stapes fits into the *fenestra vestibuli* (*ovalis*). Ligaments unite the ossicles to each other and to the adjacent walls of the tympanum. The ossicles are mobile.

Structures communicating with the middle ear include:

(*a*) The *mastoid antrum*, an air-filled cavity above and behind the tympanum with which it communicates. The *mastoid air cells* open into the antrum.

(*b*) The *auditory* (*Eustachian*) *tube*, $1\frac{1}{2}''$ long, passes from the naso-pharynx to the middle ear, allowing passage of air from the throat to the ear, thus equalising air pressure on both sides of the drum.

3. The *internal ear* is entirely enclosed in the petrous portion of the temporal bone. It consists of the *osseous labyrinth*, enclosing the *membranous labyrinth*. *Peril lymph* lies between the osseous and membranous labyrinths; the membranous labyrinth contains *endolymph*. The osseous labyrinth consists of:

(*a*) The *vestibule* or central part. On its outer wall is the *fenestra vestibuli* closed by the base of the stapes. Posteriorly are the openings of

(*b*) The 3 *semicircular canals* (anterior (superior), posterior, and lateral). These are arched osseous structures, and open into the vestibule by 5 openings. The *vestibular* branches of the 8th nerve terminate in the membranous labyrinth of the vestibule and semi-circular canals, which are concerned with the control of balance.

(*c*) The *cochlea* in front of, and communicating with, the vestibule, is a spiral canal winding $2\frac{3}{4}$ times round the *modiolus*, a hollow pillar in the petrous portion of the temporal bone. Within the canal of the cochlea is the *organ of Corti*, where the cochlear branches of the 8th nerve terminate; this is the organ of hearing.

FEMALE GENITAL ORGANS

External Genital Organs or Vulva (Fig. 26). The *mons pubis* is the eminence overlying the symphysis pubis. The *labia majora* are 2 folds of tissue, covered with skin forming, where they meet posteriorly, the *posterior commissure* or *fourchette*. The *labia minora* lie between the labia majora. The *clitoris* is a highly sensitive structure where the labia minora meet anteriorly. The *vestibule* is the space bounded anteriorly by the clitoris and on either side by the labia minora. Below the clitoris is the *urinary meatus*, and below the latter, the *vaginal orifice*.

Internal Genital Organs (Fig. 27) lie in the true pelvis. The **Vagina** is a distensible muscular canal, lined with mucous membrane, passing upwards and backwards from the vulva. Its anterior wall measures $3''$ to $3\frac{1}{2}''$, the posterior wall $3\frac{1}{2}''$ to $4''$. The upper end widens to receive the neck of the uterus. The *hymen* is a soft fibrous membrane partially surrounding the vaginal orifice in the virgin. The *greater vestibular* (*Bartholin's*) *glands*, one on each side near the entrance to the vagina, open on to the labia minora.

Relations of the vagina:

Anteriorly, the bladder is loosely attached to the upper $1''$, the urethra closely attached to the lower $1\frac{1}{2}''$.

Posteriorly, the upper $1''$ lies adjacent to the rectouterine pouch (of

Douglas), the mid portion to the rectum, and the lower 1″ to the perineal body (the central tendon of the perineum).

Laterally, lie the broad ligaments, ureters, and levator ani muscles.

The Uterus is a pear-shaped muscular organ, 3″ long by 2″ wide by 1″ thick, occupying the centre of the true pelvis, with the bladder in front and the rectum behind. It has an outer covering of peritoneum and its narrow cavity is lined by *endometrium.* The *fundus* is the broad upper end, and the *body,* the central portion; the *cervix* (1″ long) or neck projects into the vagina. Recesses of the vagina, the *anterior, posterior* and *lateral fornices* surround the cervix. The *external os* is the opening of the cervix into the vagina, the *internal os* the opening into the uterus. The uterus is normally anteverted, i.e. bent forwards over the bladder. It is held thus by 4 pairs of ligaments:

2 *broad ligaments* are folds of peritoneum, passing from the lateral margin of the uterus to the sides of the pelvis and supporting between their layers the uterus, uterine tubes, vessels and nerves.

2 *round ligaments* (R. and L.) pass from the superior angles of the uterus, down through the inguinal canals to terminate in the labia. These maintain a forward pull on the body of the uterus.

2 *utero-sacral ligaments* pass back from uterus to the rectum and sacrum.

2 *vesico-uterine ligaments* pass between the bladder and the uterus.

R. and L. Uterine Tubes (4″ long) are muscular tubes, covered by peritoneum and lined with mucous membrane (ciliated epithelium). The free or *fimbriated* ends are dilated and form fringe-like processes, *the fimbriae.* The uterine tubes transport the ova from the ovaries to the cavity of the uterus.

R. and L. Ovaries, each about the size and shape of shelled almonds, lie close to the fimbriated ends of the tubes, attached to the superior angles of the uterus by the *ovarian ligaments* and to the back of the broad ligament by the *mesovarium.* They consist of masses of minute sacs, the *ovarian (Graafian) follicles,* supported in a stroma. Each ovarian follicle contains *liquor folliculi* and an *ovum.*

The ovaries:

(*a*) Nourish the developing ova, and expel one ovum every 28 days during reproductive life;

(*b*) Produce hormones influencing the secondary sex characteristics and controlling the changes in the ovarian follicles and uterus during the menstrual cycle.

MALE GENITAL ORGANS

The Testes or Testicles are the essential male reproductive glands. They develop in the abdomen and about the seventh month of intra-uterine life they descend via the inguinal canals into the scrotum, where they are supported by the *spermatic cords.* Spermatazoa, the male sex cells, are formed in the fine seminiferous tubules within the testis and pass out through the efferent ducts of the testis into the epididymis. Hormones, which control the secondary sex characteristics of the male, are produced by the interstitial cells in the testis.

The Scrotum is a pouch-like organ containing the testes. It is divided by a fibrous septum into two cavities. Its covering skin is continuous with that of the groins and perineum. It is lined by a serous membrane, the *tunica vaginalis*, which is reflected over the testes.

The Epididymes; each is a fine convoluted tubule, the *duct of the epididymis* (20 feet long), forming an elongated mass above and behind the testis. The efferent ducts of the testis enter the head of the epididymis and the vas (ductus) deferens emerges as the continuation of the duct of the epididymis at the tail or lower end of the epididymis.

The Vasa Deferentia run up behind the epididymes, enter the abdominal cavity through the inguinal canals and descend into the pelvis.

The Seminal Vesicles are 2 sacculated pouches of the vasa deferentia lying between the base of the bladder and the rectum. They add their secretion to the semen.

The Ducts of the Seminal Vesicles join the vasa deferentia to form the

Ejaculatory Ducts which pass forwards and downwards through the prostate gland and open into the urethra.

The Prostate Gland is about the size and shape of a chestnut. It is enveloped by a fibrous capsule and surrounds the neck of the bladder and first part of the urethra. Its secretion is passed into the urethra by several small ducts. The prostate tends to enlarge after middle life and may, by projecting into the bladder, produce retention of urine.

The Bulbo-urethral (Cowper's) Glands are 2 small bodies, each about the size of a pea, one on each side of, and behind, the urethra. Their secretion also passes into the urethra.

Thus the spermatozoa pass via the epididymes, vasa deferentia, ejaculatory ducts and urethra, mixing with the secretions of the seminal vesicles, prostate and bulbo-urethral glands to form the *semen* or *seminal fluid*.

The Urethra in the male measures 6″ to 8″ long. It leaves the bladder, traverses the prostate gland (this prostatic portion is $1\frac{1}{4}$″ long) and passes into the penis.

The Penis is suspended in front of the scrotum. The root of the penis is connected to the pubic rami by the *crura*, and to the symphysis pubis by the *suspensory ligament*. At the extremity of the penis is a slight swelling, the *glans penis*. The *prepuce* or *foreskin* is the loose double fold of skin which covers the glans penis.

PRINTED IN GREAT BRITAIN BY ROBERT MACLEHOSE AND CO. LTD
THE UNIVERSITY PRESS, GLASGOW